Interactive Physics Demonstrations

a collection of *Deck the Halls* columns
and other articles reprinted from
The Physics Teacher
1972 – 2001

edited by

Joe Pizzo
Lamar University
Beaumont, Texas

Interactive Physics Demonstrations

a collection of *Deck the Halls* columns and other articles
reprinted from *The Physics Teacher*, 1972-2001

Published and Distributed by:
American Association of Physics Teachers
One Physics Ellipse
College Park, MD 20740-3845
301-209-3300
U.S.A.
www.aapt.org

Cover design by Foster & Foster, Inc.; *www.fostercovers.com*

ISBN 1-931024-00-6

Preface

"Interactive Physics Demonstrations" is mainly a collection of articles that appeared in the "Deck the Halls" column of *The Physics Teacher* from 1986 to 1996. The idea behind this column was to provide a forum for educators who had designed, constructed, and installed "stand-alone" interactive hallway demonstrations at their institutions. The "Deck the Halls" column allowed them to share the details of their work with other teachers.

Even though the column no longer appears in print, many requests have been submitted to the former column editor for reprints of individual articles or, in some cases, "everything you have on the subject." All of the "Deck the Halls" columns and a few extra articles on the subject have now been collected into this book where they are readily accessible to physics teachers.

This book includes a short introductory chapter on the history and philosophy of interactive physics demonstrations, as well as some hints on graphics, safety, and maintenance of unattended exhibits. This is followed by the collection of articles in a typical sequence of physics topics: Mechanics and Heat, Vibrations and Waves, Optics, Electricity, Chaos, and a collection of articles describing some "mini-museums" of interactive demonstrations within physics departments.

A short list of resources is included at the end of the book.

Table of Contents

Chapter 4   *Optics*

Chapter 5   *Electrostatics*

Chapter 6   *Chaos*

Chapter 7   *Multiple Exhibit Displays and Mini-Museums*

Chapter 8   Resources

Introduction:
The History and Philosophy of Interactive Physics Hallway Exhibits

The History and Philosophy of Interactive Physics Hallway Exhibits

The "interactive physics hallway exhibit" (or simply, hallway demonstration) occupies a unique place in science education. It is quite unlike a classic physics demonstration, performed by a teacher for a group of students. It is a demonstration of a single physics concept or a group of related concepts designed to stand alone (usually in a hallway or else in an available room) and invite manipulation by anyone passing by. Without supervision! As such, interactive demonstrations are closely related to the exhibits in a "hands-on" science museum. In fact, many interactive demonstrations have their genesis in a science museum exhibit.

The concept of a hands-on science exhibit was pioneered and popularized by Frank Oppenheimer, who created the Exploratorium in 1969. Prior to that time, exhibits in a science museum were, for the most part, static and passive in nature. A pane of glass separated you from the exhibit. You read the precisely constructed text, or pressed a button to hear an explanation or illuminate objects. There was no sense of being able to discover something for yourself.

Frank Oppenheimer believed in making natural phenomena and processes available and accessible. He dared to put out exhibits that could be touched and manipulated by the museum visitor. You were allowed to learn as little or as much as you wanted. The Exploratorium was, in Frank's words, "a playful museum."[1]

It is this spirit that defines a hallway demonstration. According to an ancient proverb:

I hear, I forget.
I see, I remember.
I do, I understand.

The philosophy of a hallway demonstration is one of learning by doing. A typical hallway demonstration consists of a physical phenomenon or process that is set up in an area accessible to passersby and is open to their manipulation. It should not be rigorously structured. It should be open ended, inviting the passerby to explore and play.

This is an awesome amount of freedom allowed to the participant — a freedom that makes discovery a joy but also requires a responsibility in the thoughtful design of the exhibit.

The design and construction of hallway demonstrations

Since a hallway exhibit will stand on its own without supervision, it should be attractive enough to entice someone to stop and investigate — without being overwhelming and pretentious. The construction should be rugged and attention paid to safety. Remember, people will be using this apparatus without supervision. Always assume that someone will use the equipment in the most absurd, unintended way — because they will! Ask yourself, "If abused in this way will there be a danger involved? Will the equipment break down?" If the answer is yes to either question, correct the potential problem or do not install the exhibit.

The reward in a hallway demonstration will be in direct proportion to the number of things that can be manipulated. Give the visitor a variety of ways to use the demonstration if possible. Keep adding to the number of exhibits "on the floor." There appears to be a critical mass at which point passersby decide this is not just equipment that someone forgot to take in, but is part of a plan. (It also seems that as the number of exhibits increases, the incidence of vandalism decreases.) As you add to the number of exhibits, try to install some that relate to each other. One of the joys of discovery is in discovering connections or patterns.

Check the exhibits on a regular interval. If you find one that is not functioning, remove it and repair it. Nothing is more frustrating than an exhibit that doesn't work.

Graphics are necessary as guidance to the visitor. However, use a minimum of graphics. It's sad, but it's a fact: Most people (unlike you and me) do not like to read. If the graphics are too verbose or didactic, a passerby will not look at them, or may even walk away without interacting with the exhibit. Do not be too concerned that the demonstration will be used in the wrong way or that the user will not come away with a complete understanding of the physics. The point of a hallway exhibit is simply to expose someone to the phenomenon or process and let them decide how to explore it. Even if they get nothing out of it today, they may tomorrow when they encounter the concept again or see a related phenomenon.

The Exploratorium has an excellent model for graphics with a simple *"To Do,"* *"What is Going On?"* and *"So What."* (Examples of these can be found in the Exploratorium Cookbooks which are listed in the chapter on resources.) These point out what you can manipulate and what to look for and what that might demonstrate. Their graphics also call attention to related exhibits when appropriate. Photographs of someone actually using the exhibit can be extremely helpful and worth more words than you could ever write.

1.   Frank Oppenheimer, *Am. J. Phys.* **40**, 978 (1972).

Mechanics and Heat

Bowling Ball Impact Apparatus

Roy Biser, 107 South Elk, Fredricksburg, TX 78624

Many people, at one time or another, have used a demonstration piece called the "Impact Ball Apparatus," or have played with a commercial version, called an "Executive Desk Toy." Fig. 1 shows a scaled-up version which has been built as a hallway demonstration. The apparatus pictured consists of a row of bowling balls that just touch one another and are suspended in such a way that all the balls swing in the same plane.

A number of the balls can be drawn to one side, released, and allowed to strike the remaining group. After collision, the same number of balls fly out from the other side, all others remaining almost at rest. What this demonstration actually shows is not as simple as one might think at first sight. Chapman has developed an extensive analysis of all the physics involved, and the interested reader should refer to his paper.[1] Since the target audience of hallway demonstrations is the nonscientist, the graphics with this exhibit simplify the situation and use it as an example of momentum conservation: "A combination of mass and velocity coming in equals the combination of mass and velocity going out." Participants are encouraged to experiment with different initial combinations and notice the symmetry of the situations before and after collisions.

The purpose of this article is to provide details on the construction of this apparatus. The frame consists entirely of "two by fours" with one sheet of pegboard as a background. Fig. 2 shows the back and side views of the exhibit, along with the major dimensions. Fig. 1 and Fig. 2 should provide a sufficient guideline to the final assembly of the frame. (Notice that the construction of the frame, as shown, allows the participant to step right into the apparatus.) The only tools needed for construction are hammer, nails, ruler, handsaw, and miter box.

Bowling balls without holes can be purchased from a local bowling supply shop, or with holes from garage sales. Two small holes, diametrically opposite each other, should be drilled in each ball. Eye screws, for the passage of the suspension cord, are inserted in each of these holes.

The suspension system requires the most attention to detail; the side view in Fig. 2 should serve as a reference. One end of a heavy nylon cord should be attached to a peg (screw) on the upper right of the frame (in the side view). This cord should pass through the eye screw on the left side of the ball, then around the peg on the upper left of the frame, back around through the eye screw on the right of the ball, and then be attached to the peg at the

Fig. 1. A large-scale version of the impact apparatus.

Phys. Teach. **25,** 40-41 (Jan. 1987)

Interactive Physics Demonstrations

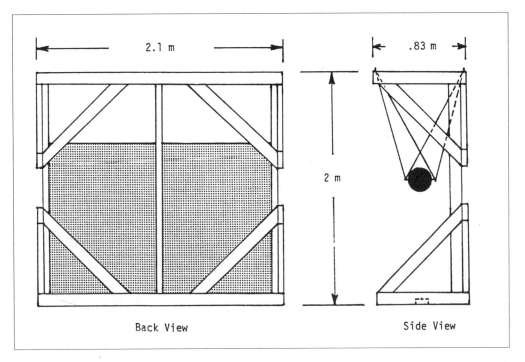

Fig. 2. Back view and side view of the Bowling Ball Impact Apparatus, showing details of construction.

starting point on the upper right of the frame. Leveling of the balls can be accomplished by making small loops of cord around the pegs on either side, as needed. A small piece of wire, clamped around the intersection of the cords, adds to the stability.

This demonstration should be placed away from areas where a high noise level is undesirable. The collisions are very noisy, and it is al-most impossible for anyone to pass this demonstration without some form of interaction.

Reference

1. Seville Chapman, "Misconception Concerning the Dynamics of the Impact Ball Apparatus," *Am. J. Phys.*, **28** 705 (1960).

Physics on an Air Track

Rebecca A. Koopmann and S. Maleki, Union College, Department of Physics,
Schenectady, NY 12308

When our lecture classroom was reno-
vated recently our four-meter air
track would no longer fit, and it was left in
storage to collect dust! One obvious solution to
this "waste of apparatus" was to use it for a hallway exhibit. Thus, in the summer of 1986, we
took on this challenge as a summer project.
The project was completed that fall. Since that
time our air track has gotten a great deal of use,
not only by the casual student either waiting
for a class to begin or just passing by, but also
as directed by their physics or engineering pro-
fessors. More serious students investigate the
physical principles that can be demonstrated
by this exhibit. Also, our hallway exhibit has
served to engage audiences of visiting parents,
alumni, and their youngsters, and other
passersby with fun, challenge, and (we hope)
some physics!

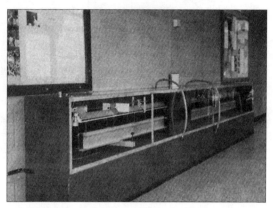

**Fig. 1. There are three different demonstrations
on our (long) air track exhibit.**

Because of the length of our air track, we
have managed to include three different interactive demonstrations: 1) elastic collision, 2)
forced oscillator, and 3) coupled oscillators
(Fig. 1). We will first discuss the general con-

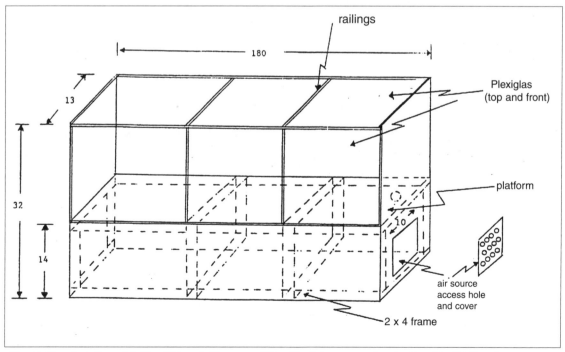

Fig. 2. Construction details of the platform and the Plexiglas cover (scale: 1 unit = 2.54 cm).

Phys. Teach. **27**, 112-115 (Feb. 1989)

Interactive Physics Demonstrations

struction of the exhibit, describe each of the demonstrations separately, and finally suggest how a similar exhibit could be constructed with a modest budget.

Construction

In our exhibit, the air track rests on a rectangular platform and is covered on all sides as if in a box (Fig. 2). Except for the top and the front side of this box, which are 0.6-cm (¼ in), the Plexiglas sheets, all the sides and the platform itself are made of 1.3-cm (6¼-in) plywood. The wooden sides are nailed to a simple frame of 2 by 4s concealed in the platform. The Plexiglas sheets are attached to 2.5-cm (1 in by 1 in) right-angle aluminum railings by machine screws and washers, and the railings are secured to the wooden frame using nuts and bolts.

The air source is placed under the platform and connected to the air track by a hose passing through a hole drilled in the top face of the platform. A 25-cm square hole was cut in the end of the platform for easy access to the air source and covered by a 0.6-cm pegboard piece to allow adequate air intake for the source. Since quiet operation of the air track was a major concern, we experimented with a variety of mufflers to reduce the noise of the air source only to discover that most of the noise was in the track itself! This noise was greatly reduced once the track was covered on all sides by the box. (This could also be a useful trick for reducing noise when an air track is used for lecture demonstrations.) The air source as well as the two motors used for forcing the oscillations (see below) are connected, through a push-button switch, to a variable timer switch. Once the button is pushed, the timer switch turns on, powering the air source and the motors for a period of about two minutes. It then automatically turns off until the button is pushed again.

Demonstrations

1. *Elastic Collision:* (Fig. 3) We have used two gliders of equal mass to demonstrate a special one-dimensional elastic collision. If one glider is initially at rest, upon impact by the second glider it will begin to move while the second glider comes to a complete stop! This effect is

Fig. 3. This top-view of the "Elastic Collision" demonstration shows the tunnel and the two gliders, each with a circular magnet mounted on its top.

dramatized in our exhibit by using two identical gliders, but of different colors, and a "tunnel." If the stationary glider is "hidden" under the tunnel, it appears as though the moving glider changes color each time it passes under the tunnel! The gliders are remotely moved along the track by means of two control bar magnets, each connected to the exhibit box by a one-meter-long brass chain. (We have found that cow magnets work very well. They are inexpensive, and smooth at the edges so they do not scratch the Plexiglas. These chains can also be covered with tygon tubing to further help protect the Plexiglas.) The bar magnets interact with two flat circular magnets each mounted on top of one of the gliders. The advantage of using a circular magnet instead of a bar magnet on the glider is that once the polarity of this

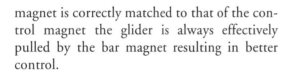

Fig. 4. Top-view of the "Forced Oscillator." Note the "Wings" used to damp glider's motion.

Fig. 5. Top-view of the "Coupled Oscillator."

magnet is correctly matched to that of the control magnet the glider is always effectively pulled by the bar magnet resulting in better control.

2. *Forced Oscillators:* (Fig. 4) In this part of the exhibit a glider is connected to identical springs at its two ends. One of the springs is held fixed while the other spring is connected to a movable arm. The arm moves back and forth along the length of the track by means of a motor. A simple mechanism similar to that used on a toy train translates the circular motion of the motor to a simple harmonic motion of the rod. The knob of the potentiometer, mounted on the top cover Plexiglas, can be turned to change the motor speed and thus the driving frequency. The instructions for this part of the exhibit give a brief explanation of the dependence of glider amplitude on the

driving frequency, then challenges the audience to locate the resonance frequency for which the amplitude of the glider will reach its maximum value. We used two cardboard "wings" (3-mm thick; 7.5 cm by 5 cm) on the two sides of the glider to damp its motion in order to more rapidly suppress off-resonance oscillations. We have found that even with this modification only our most conscientious audience has the patience to locate the resonance frequency! To remove this frustration factor, it might be better to include the knob position corresponding to resonance in our instructions, but we feel that this would also remove the elements of challenge and surprise.

3. *Coupled Oscillators:* (Fig. 5) This part of the exhibit is similar to the previous part except that now the single glider is replaced with two identical gliders connected by a third spring,

Interactive Physics Demonstrations

which is the same as the two end springs. As in the case of the forced oscillator, both the amplitude and the frequency of these gliders is a function of the driving frequency. For almost all driving frequencies, the two gliders oscillate with different frequencies and with amplitudes that change with time. However, there are two distinct driving frequencies at which the two gliders oscillate with equal frequencies (normal modes) and constant amplitudes. The challenge in this demonstration is to change the driving frequency in order to locate the two normal modes of oscillation. While in one normal mode (the symmetric or "translational" mode) the two gliders oscillate back and forth in phase (similar to the single glider at resonance), in the second normal mode (the antisymmetric or "breathing" mode) the gliders oscillate 180° out of phase with each other.

Suggestion

Although not every school has an ideal four-meter air track which can be committed for use as a hallway exhibit, most schools have at least one shorter air track that might be borrowed for such purposes. When not otherwise in use in laboratory or classroom, this air track could be stored in a hallway exhibit box similar to ours.

The Plexiglas cover could be hinged to the wooden frame so that the track could be easily removed when it is needed elsewhere. The three different demonstrations described here could be used one at a time over the course of the year to give variety to the exhibit. An easily changeable exhibit of this kind would allow the investigation of different aspects of collisions simply by changing gliders and bumpers. Likewise, the third part of our setup could be easily modified by just changing springs and gliders to permit the investigation of many different and interesting aspects of coupled oscillations.

A Long Precision Air Track

Fritz Schoch and Walter Winiger, Kantonsschule Heerbrugg, CH-9435 Heerbrugg, Switzerland

A recent article in the "Deck the Halls" column of *The Physics Teacher*[1] described three interactive demonstrations on a 4-m air track that is set up in a hallway at Union College.

For those who have the space, we would like to share the details for constructing a much longer precision air track for interactive use in a hallway.

We recently finished the construction of a very accurate air track with a length of 8.6 m. It stands in the corridor leading to the physics lecture room (Fig. 1). The air track consists of three parts of approximately 3 m each, which are connected by shafts that allow some axial movements, as shown in Fig. 2. This is done so precisely that there is practically no difference in height between adjoining pieces. The quadratic aluminum profile is mounted on supports about 150 mm in height to isolate the track, which undergoes thermal expansion, from the supporting

Fig. 1. Long Swiss precision air track with a length of 8.6 m.

Phys. Teach. **28**, 618 (Dec. 1990)

steel beam.

The air pressure of about 2.5 bar is supplied by a compressor, which is located in our workshop and therefore cannot be heard in the area of the track.

There are about 700 predrilled holes with a diameter of 1 mm each for the air to get out. Cheap ruby watch stones with an outer diameter of 1 mm and an inner diameter of approximately 0.1 mm were inserted into the 700 predrilled holes. We use heavy (1 kg) aluminum gliders that we can load up to a maximum of more than 2 kg.

The entire air track can be tilted by about five degrees in either direction in order for inclined plane demonstrations to be easily performed. Details of the construction are shown in Fig. 3. The critical parts that we could not manufacture in our physics workshops were made by the nearby firm, WILD, famous for producing Swiss precision theodolites. It has been our experience that industry is very helpful in any respect concerning the education of our students.

Our air track has been operating excellently for over a year. It is certainly one of the longest ever used for educational purposes.

Reference

1.   Rebecca A. Koopman and S. Maleki, *Phys. Teach.* **27**, 112 (1989).

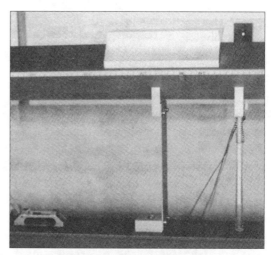

Fig. 2. Adjoining pieces. Also shown are a photogate and the aluminum legs used to compensate for variation in the ambient temperature (from 15°C to 30°C).

Fig. 3. Device to tilt the air track.

Skiing Revisited — To Lean or Not to Lean?

Phillip W. Gronseth and Marc A. Hallada, United States Air Force Academy, Colorado Springs, CO 80840-5701

Recent issues of *The Physics Teacher* have contained discussions of why a ski instructor teaches students to lean forward when skiing downhill.[1,2] Because the Air Force Academy is located in an area where skiing is an activity for almost all our students, we constructed a simple hallway demonstration to prove the point.

Our exhibit is designed to give a "hands-on" demonstration of the concepts discussed in the article by Bartlett and Hewitt. The setup consists of a semicircular ramp and two cars (Fig. 1). One car has a small, critically damped pendulum on it. The other car has a plastic bottle containing colored water. When the cars are rolling back and forth on the ramp, the pendulum points toward the ramp (not the floor) and the surface of the liquid is tangent to the ramp (not parallel to the floor). Many students react with disbelief. The ensuing discussion is quite vocal and often carries over into the classroom — to the benefit of all involved.

The graphics for this demonstration consist of several diagrams showing situations inside a house rolling without resistance down an incline. These diagrams were reproduced from the article by Bartlett and Hewitt. Along with each diagram we have placed some thought-provoking questions. To prove that a lamp would hang perpendicular to the ceiling, instructions are given to try the toy car with the pendulum on the track. To illustrate that the surface of water in a bathtub would be parallel to the inclined plane, the participant is instructed to try the toy car with the bottle of colored water on the track.

In the graphics, we leave a last thought, "What happens in deep powder?" Pictures are included, showing skiers on hardpack snow (leaning forward) and on deep-powder snow ("sitting back"). The participant is asked,

Fig. 1. The setup for a hallway demonstration on skiing downhill.

"Why do ski instructors often say to 'sit back' in deep powder?"

A common answer to this question is, "to prevent the ski tips from digging deeper into the snow." Although that answer is certainly true, digging tips deeper into the snow is merely a symptom of the skier not balancing the forces. In deep powder, the frictional drag is substantially greater than on hardpack. Thus, the skier may actually reach a terminal velocity. The skier then will be in equilibrium when standing parallel to the pine trees (i.e., when "sitting back"). Presumably, a skier on hardpack also would have to "sit back" if he or she were brave enough to reach terminal velocity. However, with the minimal drag that the hardpack and air offer, it is debatable whether such a skier would be brave or foolish.

References

1. Albert A. Bartlett and Paul G. Hewitt, "Why the Ski Instructor Says 'Lean Forward!'" *Phys. Teach.* **25**, 28 (1987).

2. *Phys. Teach.* **26**, 71 (1988).

Phys. Teach. **26**, 584 (Dec. 1988)

Elevator Exhibit*

Laurie Eason and Alan J. Friedman, Lawrence Hall of Science, University of California,
Berkeley, CA 94720

Purpose

This exhibit is designed to improve the public's understanding of several concepts described by Newton's second law, taking advantage of an under-utilized physics observatory: the common elevator.

The exhibit can be installed in any elevator in any public building and is designed for use by the public at large. A portable model would allow for field trip use by physics instructors who do not have immediate access to an elevator.

Primary Attributes: The exhibit is installed in an elevator to present information about physics during the normally boring wait for, and ride in, the elevator. The concepts are presented in simple terms, and the user's physical participation is central. Newton's second law is related to the user's direct experience by encouraging him/her to measure his/her own change in weight during the elevator ride, and by observing the behavior of an elementary balance and a spring scale.

Secondary Attributes: This exhibit also presents a demonstration of the measurement of mass and force including metric units in kilograms and newtons on the balance and spring scale. The exhibit alludes to Newton's other laws and is open-ended to encourage experimental activities such as determining a time history of the acceleration of the elevator.

Specifications

The exhibit contains three components:

1. A single-pivot, rigid beam balance comparing two 1-kg weights.
2. An exposed-spring scale measuring the force, in newtons, to support a 1-kg weight.

---

*This exhibit was one of the three winners in the AAPT-APS "Store-Front Physics" Contest concluded at the 1975 Anaheim meeting.

Phys. Teach. **13**, 492-493 (Nov. 1975)

Fig. 1. The elevator in use.

3. An ordinary bathroom scale for the user to weigh him/herself, in pounds.

Figure 1 shows the basic configuration.

Text is provided outside the elevator at the call buttons to prepare the user for the exhibit experience, and inside the elevator for each of the three components. The particular script used will depend on the concepts to be explored and the sophistication of the audience. We presented definitions of force, weight, and

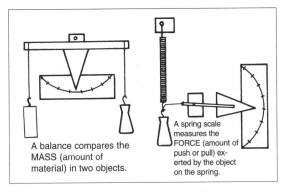

A balance compares the MASS (amount of material) in two objects.

A spring scale measures the FORCE (amount of push or pull) exerted by the object on the spring.

Fig. 2. Components of the wall display.

mass, and asked the users leading questions such as how their weight on the bathroom scale would change,[1] or how mass and force are distinguished by the behavior of the balance and scales.

There is one cardinal rule for successful exhibits of this type: the script must be kept short. We used 35 words outside the elevator, and a total of 40 to 50 words inside (depending on the concepts presented). Directions must be simple and direct to stimulate audience participation. The script should encourage exploitation of the concepts presented rather than observation only to confirm the test.

Evaluation

We evaluated the effectiveness of this exhibit by repeating two phases: a questionnaire-survey, supplemented by interviews; and redesign of the exhibit based on results of phase 1. The scripts changed significantly as a result of this procedure.[2] We concluded that the exhibit does stimulate curiosity and learning about the relationship between mass, weight, and acceleration.

Replication

This exhibit is entirely mechanical and was assembled in about eight hours, using available materials from our wood shop. No critical parts or dimensions are involved. Construction is simple and would make an excellent student project.

Script: The text, less than 100 words in all, was typed on cards using a large-type typewriter.

Floor scale: We used an ordinary "bathroom" scale. A higher quality scale would alleviate a problem of reduced sensitivity to changes for users below 50 or above 200 pounds. It would also be desirable to have a scale in newtons or newtons and pounds. The scale was attached to the elevator using a 1-m length of chain to discourage theft.

Wall display: This item consisted of two parts — a spring scale and a balance. A Plexiglas and wood box was used to mount them on the wall. These are shown in Fig. 2. A portable model should be equipped with legs to present the box at a comfortable viewing height.

Our exhibit was designed to be unattended; protective measures such as the chain and the Plexiglas cover would not be needed in a laboratory situation.

The spring scale weighs a 1-kg steel mass. We used a spring with 10 cm unstretched length, and 20-cm length with a 1-kg mass suspended. The change in length of any Hooke's law spring for a given fractional change in the effective g is dependent only on the equilibrium extension of the spring from its unstretched length (proof left as an exercise for the reader). One need only decide on the sensitivity desired and select any spring that can be stretched to the corresponding extension within its Hooke's law range.

A typical elevator produces accelerations

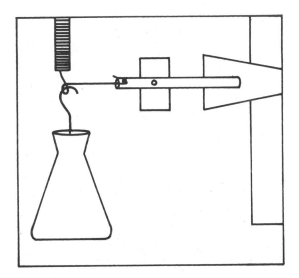

Fig. 3. Detail of the spring and pointer amplifier system.

that increase or decrease the effective g by about 5%, and this should be immediately noticeable on the spring balance in the exhibit. To make the 0.5-cm length change for our spring more apparent, a lever amplifier was added to the spring. This lever would not be needed if a longer spring configuration (say 1-m long) were used. In our case the lever is a wood strip with a cardboard arrow on one end. The pivot is a nail through a hole in the strip with a nylon sleeve around the nail to reduce friction. The pivot is 1.5 cm from one end of the strip, and 0.5 cm from that end a small hole was drilled parallel to the pivot hole. The spring was "unwrapped" to provide a hook to hold the 1-kg mass and to extend that junction to the small hole in the strip (see Fig. 3). Since the cardboard arrow ends 10 cm from the pivot on the other end of the strip, this results in a lever-amplifier of 10 times. Thus the arrow moves about 5 cm as the elevator starts and stops. A cardboard scale is calibrated to indicate forces from 9 to 11 N. A piece of cardboard is behind the weight and rubs against it lightly to damp out oscillations.

The balance is designed to compare two 1-kg steel weights.[3] It consists of a rigid wood beam, 25 cm long, and a cardboard pointer and scale. The beam is pivoted on a nail through a hole about 1 cm above the points on the beam from which the weights hang. This dimension determines the sensitivity of the balance, and was selected to provide the same amount of pointer motion for a given change of mass on one side that the spring scale would show for the same change in its load. Increasing the height of the pivot above the points from which the weights hang will decrease the sensitivity of the balance. Unlike a normal laboratory balance, we calibrated the scale in kilograms, 0.9 to 1.1, for the left-hand mass. (A normal balance shows only null.) Our combination of mass, lever arm, nylon-nail pivot, and elevator vibration results in continuous pointer oscillation over a 1-mm range, which is necessary to show that the balance is not glued in place. (Many people expect it to shift as the elevator accelerates.)[4]

Notes

1. There is considerable controversy concerning the definitions of weight and mass. Exhibit designers beware!

2. Survey results and our current script are available from the authors.

3. Jayne Knoche of Florida State University has recommended that the two masses be of different shapes and density to reinforce the concept that only the mass must remain constant to keep the beam in balance.

4. We have heard (personal correspondence) that other institutions may have used exhibits with components similar to ours, but we have not found any published descriptions.

Pulsed Water Streams Under Stroboscopic Light

Andrew Graham, Department of Physics and Astronomy,
Appalachian State University, Boone, NC 28608

The Water Drop Generator (designed by Harold E. Edgerton, MIT) is a classic demonstration that has been used for years to grab attention and stimulate curiosity.[1] The Generator produces a column of large, well-defined water drops that appear to be a continuous stream of water under normal lighting. Illumination of the column with a strobe light set at the frequency of the pump (60 Hz) creates the illusion of a series of stationary drops suspended in midair, as seen in Fig. 1. Increasing the strobe frequency slightly makes the drops appear to move upward from the collector to the nozzle, defying our knowledge that things fall down, not up. For strobe frequencies slightly slower than 60 Hz, the drops appear to drift slowly downward.

The Generator can be used in a hallway showcase with the strobe connected to an external control accessible to the observer. The strobe used in our setup is a 1531-AB Strobotac by General Radio. The external control is a Hewlett Packard Model 209-A Oscillator that sits outside the showcase. The strobe is set for external input, medium range position, and is connected to the oscillator through the external trigger jack. The oscillator range is set for X10 Hz, which allows the observer to vary the strobe frequency from 20 to 200 Hz. With these frequencies, the drops can be made to go up and down, or remain stationary. (A point concerning the safe use of strobes: It is my understanding that strobe frequencies from about 8 to 12 Hz can induce seizures in a small percentage of people. For that reason, I remove the range selector knob from the oscillator to prevent access to the lower frequencies.)

It is a truly enlightening experience to sit near the showcase with a cup of coffee and the morning paper, appearing to be totally uninter-

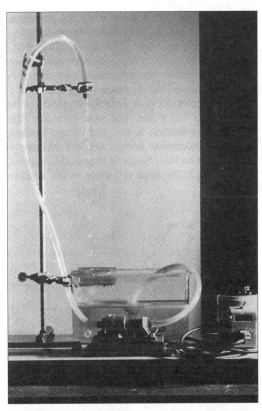

Fig. 1. The normal Water Drop Generator. The drops are produced by pulses from the magnetically driven oscillating pump. The tube must be supported so that the pulses are not dampened out. Only trial and error will tell where the supports should go to make the best patterns. Notice the top support is a rubber band.

ested, and listen to students attempt to explain how the water drops can go up.

The Generator also makes a good demonstration for the classroom, especially when discussing the acceleration due to gravity. When the water drops are made to appear stationary, it is apparent that the spacing between the drops is not constant but progressively increases from the top to the bottom. Measuring the

Phys. Teach. **25**, 512-513 (Nov. 1987)

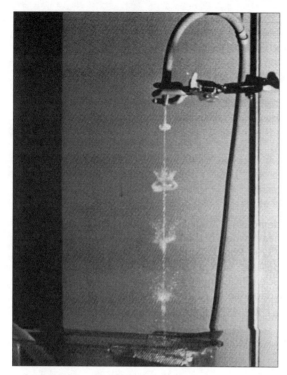

Fig. 2. With a soft rubber tube and higher velocity nozzle, the Water Drop Generator no longer produces drops. The result of this modification is a very thin and delicate water film with a shape very similar to a rose, hence the name The Water Rose.

distances between the drops and using the fact that the drops are 1/60th of a second apart in time permits a rough calculation of g with an accuracy of about 10%.

A simple modification to the basic Generator setup will produce some unbelievably beautiful water patterns (Fig. 2). The modification requires replacing the Tygon outlet and nozzle from the regular setup with a thin-wall soft rubber tube and a nozzle with a smaller diameter exit port. The same rod and support hardware may be used for both setups. With the new nozzle the water exits at much higher velocity and subsequently does not form distinct drops but remains in the form of a stream. The Water Rose is the pattern formed when a bulge develops on the stream due to the pressure pulse from the pump. The front part of the bulge slows down, the rear part rides up over the front and creates a type of cresting wave. Then air resistance apparently forces the wave to spread out and then up, pulling the bulge into a very thin film with a shape similar to a

rose. The film is very delicate and rapidly disintegrates into droplets.

Many possibilities exist for exhibits that are modifications of the basic Generator.

Constructing the Water Drop Generator

Pump: Available from Cole Parmer Instrument Company, Chicago, IL 60648. 1987 Cat. No. 7103-10, $78.95.

Tubing: Plastic or rubber thin wall, 16 mm x 13 mm (o.d. 5/8 in, i.d. 1/2 in) approximately 1 m for outlet, 0.75 m to 1 m for intake. Available from hardware stores or most chemical supply companies.

Nozzle: Brass, 30 mm (1.25 in), 13 mm (½ in o.d.), i.d. tapered from 13 mm (½ in) down to 8 mm (5/16 in). Available from Robert Miller, Rt. 2. Box 901, Boone, NC 28607, $5 plus $1 shipping.

Setup: The support is a standard 0.75-m rod with T-base mounted firmly onto a wooden base. Pump vibration is a frustrating problem with this setup, so the pump must be attached so that vibration and shifting are minimized. (The rubber suction cup feet will not hold the pump in place.) This can be accomplished by securing the pump base to the wooden base with two screws that have rubber sleeves around them, made from small rubber tubing. The screws should not be tight against the pump base. A three-finger clamp may be used to support the nozzle. Rubber bands may be used for further support of the tubing if needed. The tube should not be allowed to touch anything or the pulses from the pump will be dampened. Use a plastic trough for the collector so that the pickup tube can be positioned away from the point where the drops enter. This will prevent air bubbles from entering the pickup tube. A piece of wire screen placed across the trough will break up the drops before they strike the water and eliminate most splatter. (While operating the strobe so that the drops appear to go up, notice that spray patterns underneath the screen rise and pass through the screen, transformed into water drops, defying gravity AND reducing entropy!)

Adding a *very small* amount of Fluorescein Disodium Salt gives the water a nice green glow and makes the drops more visible. It is helpful to plug the pump into a Variac to permit adjusting the amplitude of the pressure pulses from the pump.

Modification: The nozzle for making the Water Rose patterns can be made from the cap of a Bic pen. The bulge forming the pocket clip must be trimmed away and the top cut off approximately 6 mm from the end. This will leave a small hole of approximately the correct diameter. A brass nozzle that makes cleaner patterns can be ordered from Robert Miller (see above address); $5 plus $1 shipping. The rubber tubing is 8 mm (5/16 in) inside diameter with a 1.6-mm (1.16-in) wall thickness;

Fisher Scientific No. 14-166D. To make the best Rose patterns will require looping a rubber band around the rubber tube near the highest point and supporting the rubber band from an arm attached to the main support rod. This allows both the tension on the tube and its position to be changed. Small changes in tension or position can make dramatic changes in the water patterns.

Acknowledgments

Cover photo by Appalachian State University photographer Mike Rominger. Fig. 1 and Fig. 2 by Eccles Wall, ASU physics student.

References

1. Harold Edgerton, *Electronic Flash, Strobe*, 2nd ed. (The MIT Press, Cambridge, MA and London, England) p. 161.

Hallway Projectile Demonstrator

Peter M. Hall, Department of Chemistry and Physics, Johnson C. Smith University, 100 Beatties Ford Road, Charlotte, NC 28216

Students regularly see physics in action at the water fountain. Here they have a beautiful example of a classical parabolic trajectory right under their noses! I photographed the arc with a meter stick behind it, and posted it above the fountain with the challenge to find the magnitude and direction of the velocity as the water leaves the fixture (point A). I also asked students to provide an equation for the trajectory. I handed out enlarged photocopies of the original for each student to work on at home. The problem related physics to everyday life, and shows how much can be learned from a relatively small amount of data. One can easily calculate both the *x* and *y* components of the velocity, the time to reach the highest point, and the angle of the initial velocity. The calculated angle can be compared with the angle measured on the photograph.

More advanced students might notice the

Fig. 1. Can you calculate the speed of the water at point A? Can you write an equation for the trajectory?

water "bunching up" on the ascent, and "thinning out" on the descent, to the point of droplet separation. This is consistent with the concept that the flow (mass per unit time) equals the product of the speed, cross-sectional area, and density. And since the density and flow stay constant throughout the trajectory, the cross-sectional area must vary inversely as the speed. A plot of the speed as a function of time would make this point clear.

Phys. Teach. **30**, 167 (March 1992)

Bernoulli Station

Joe Pizzo, Department of Physics, Lamar University, Beaumont, TX 77710

When air sweeps across a surface at a high speed, the pressure on that surface is lowered. This phenomenon is commonly referred to as the Bernoulli effect. The Bernoulli effect is the subject of some of the most intriguing demonstrations in physics. Bernoulli Station (shown in Fig. 1) gives participants the opportunity not only to see this effect, but to actually *feel* the pressure differential between two sides of an object caused by the rapid flow of air across one side.

Bernoulli Station is also a prime example of recycling discarded items to provide hallway demonstrations at minimum cost. Rescued from oblivion for this exhibit were an old dresser with broken legs, a shop vacuum cleaner (shown inside the "gutted" dresser in Fig. 2), a drain hose from a washing machine, and a small piece of paneling. (The only expense was $5 for the "shop vac," which was bought at a garage sale.)

Construction

The high-speed air stream is obtained by connecting one end of a hose to the blower side of the "shop vac." The other side of the hose is adapted to a short length of small diameter PVC pipe as shown in Fig. 3. The broken legs of the dresser were removed and space inside was made for the vacuum cleaner and hose assembly (see Fig. 2). A hole was drilled through the top of the dresser to accommodate the PVC fitting by friction. After the small piece of PVC pipe had been inserted into the hole so that it was flush with the dresser surface (shown in Fig. 1, below the ball), the hose with adapter was attached from within and secured by friction and duct tape. When this assembly was completed, the facade of the dresser was restored and the drawer panels glued shut.

Fig. 1. The "Bernoulli Station."

Fig. 2. A discarded dresser has its legs removed and insides "gutted" to accommodate the air supply for the Bernoulli Station.

Use

Several different experiments can be done at this station.

(a) A beach ball can be left suspended over the air stream (as shown in Fig. 1). Participants can push the ball gently to one side and feel the restoring force due to the higher atmospheric pressure on the side of the ball away from the air stream.

(b) A piece of drain hose can be inserted into the hole as shown in Fig. 4 and flexed to direct the ball to the side as shown in Fig. 5. Manipulation of the drain hose by the par-

Phys. Teach. **27**, 308-310 (April 1989)

Fig. 3. The hose from the air blower is connected to a small length of small diameter PVC pipe by a PVC adapter.

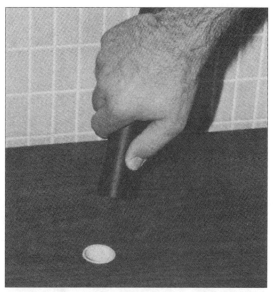

Fig. 4. A piece of washing machine drain hose fits snugly into the "air hole."

Fig. 5. The drain hose can be flexed to direct the air stream.

ticipant will cause the ball to move to different positions, suspended with no apparent support.

(c) If the experiment is set up as in part (b), and the flexed hose left unattended as shown in Fig. 6, a chaotic behavior that I call the "Bernoulli Oscillator" is created. At some points, where there is a large component of air velocity across the top of the ball, the net vertical force will be up. If the ball rises too high, the component of velocity across the top of the ball will be too small, and the net vertical force will be down. At the same time, if the ball is far enough to the left and low enough, the component of air velocity perpendicular to the left side of the ball will dominate the horizontal motion with a net force to the right. When the ball is high enough, the tangential flow across the left side of the ball will cause a net component of horizontal force to the left. The resulting motion will be a cyclic, rolling motion that never quite repeats itself. It may go on in this rolling, up-and-down motion indefinitely,

or it may venture too far to the right or left and fall. There is a very sensitive dependence on the initial conditions.

(d) Figure 7 shows how one can actually *feel* the pressure differential between the top and bottom surfaces of a small piece of paneling. This is caused when one places the paneling directly on top of the air hole, forcing the air across the bottom surface with a high velocity. The participant can use the handle attached to the paneling and pull against the greater atmospheric pres-

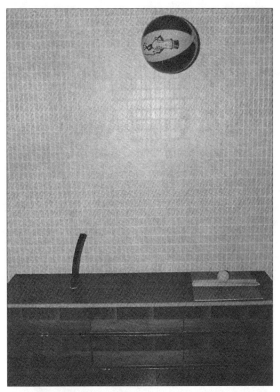

Fig. 6. When the drain hose directing the air stream is left bent to the side, the system forms a "Bernoulli Oscillator."

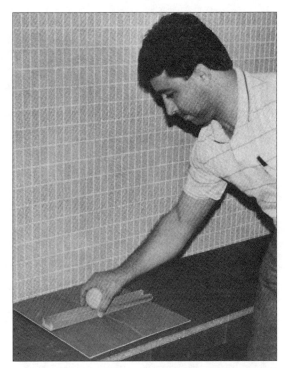

Fig. 7. A small piece of paneling (with handle attached) is placed directly on the "air hole." The low pressure caused by the high velocity on the underside makes it difficult to pull the paneling up.

sure, which is exerted downward against the top of the paneling.

Graphics

Figures 1, 4, 5, and 6, which appear in this article, have also been used to instruct the participant in the operation of the exhibit. These photographs are so self-explanatory that very little additional instruction is needed.

There is a simple statement displayed: "A high rate of air flow across (not against) a surface lowers the atmospheric pressure against that surface. If the atmospheric pressure on an opposite surface is maintained at its normal value, there will be a net force tending to push the object toward the low pressure (high air flow) region. Can you see how this explains all the effects you experience in this exhibit?"

Helpful Hints

We have found the following to be helpful in the operation of this exhibit:

- An opening should be left in back for air intake into the vacuum cleaner.
- Sound insulation has been installed inside the dresser.
- An off-on switch has been installed on the surface of the dresser, although we sometimes leave the demonstration running as shown in Fig. 1 or Fig. 6 in order to catch the attention of passersby.
- It is useful to have some place to keep the ball from rolling away when it is not in use. A plastic basket has been attached to the left side of the dresser for this purpose.

Airplane Dynamics: Engine Thrust, Engine Braking, and Wing Lift

Robert Kasting, East High School, Columbus, IN 47201

This demonstration was selected as one of the "favorites" in the Frank Oppenheimer Memorial Exhibit which was held January 27-30, 1987, at the Exploratorium, San Francisco.

A fan cart (similar to Central Scientific #72717-025 as shown in the 1984-1985 Physics-Chemistry catalog) demonstrates airplane engine thrust. In addition, some simple modifications can turn this fan cart into an exploratory hallway demonstration which will also illustrate airplane engine braking and wing lift (Fig. 1). The modifications are:

1. Build an airfoil-shaped wing section using balsa wood so that the wing section will intercept the full airflow from the propeller. When the air from the propeller flows over the wing section, a net force on the wing will cause the cart to steer to the right or left depending on the orientation of the wing. Use a rubber band to hold the wing section in place, as shown in Fig. 2; the rubber band allows the wing orientation to be changed easily.

2. Build a deflector plate from material similar to aluminum flashing. An acceptable

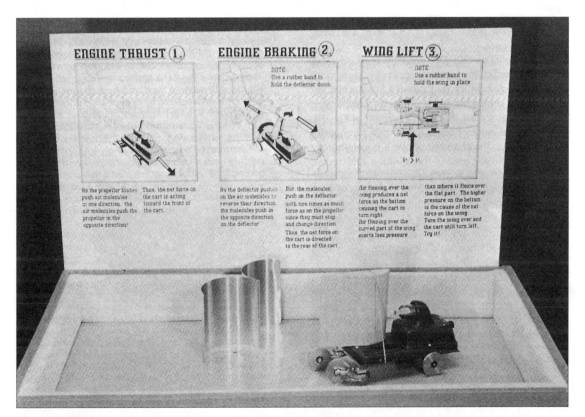

Fig. 1. A fan cart, with appropriate modifications, is used as an exploratory exhibit to demonstrate engine thrust, engine braking, and wing lift of an airplane.

Phys. Teach. **26**, 122-123 (Feb. 1988)

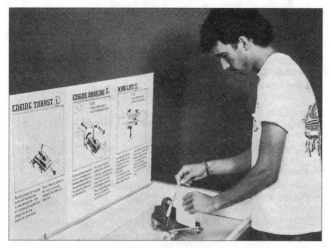

Fig. 2. A rubber band is used to hold the airfoil-shaped wing section in place, allowing the orientation to be changed easily.

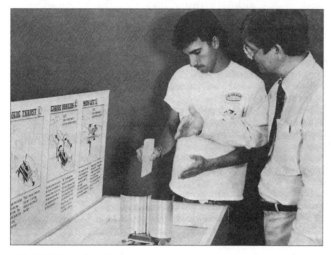

Fig. 3. When the deflector plates are used on the fan cart, airplane engine braking can be demonstrated.

shape can be obtained by first folding in half a rectangular sheet of the aluminum flashing and then wrapping each side of the fold around a can of spray paint. When the airflow from the propeller strikes the deflector plate (as positioned in Fig. 3) and is deflected in the opposite direction, there will be a net force on the cart to the rear. The deflector plate also can be held in place by a single rubber band.

3. The wheels of the cart were replaced by low-friction, ball bearing wheels because the effects to be demonstrated are weak. The wheels farthest from the propeller were further modified by attaching them to the end of bars that can move freely in a horizontal plane. Then the net force on the wing section could push that end of the cart to the right or left. This modification permits the wheels to swing around, allowing the cart to travel either forward or backward.

The edges of the experimental space for the cart were lined with 2.54-cm foam as a cushion for the inevitable crashes the cart experiences as students explore the three situations in airplane dynamics.

I used to wonder how airplanes used their engines to help in braking during the runway deceleration. When I had a chance to fly in an airplane, seated near the engine, I observed that during the runway deceleration, deflector plates are deployed and positioned in the jet blast in such a way as to deflect the jet blast toward the front of the plane, resulting in a net force on the plane to the rear. Since making this exploratory exhibit available to students, I have found that many students have the same questions that I had and are very interested in seeing this demonstration.

Rotational Motion Demonstrator

Everette E. Tompkins, La Jolla High School, San Diego, CA 92037

This demonstration was selected as one of the "favorites" in the Frank Oppenheimer Memorial Exhibit, which was held January 27-30, 1987, at the Exploratorium, San Francisco.

Aside view of a "hands-on" apparatus designed to demonstrate the conservation of angular momentum, as well as to give the operator a feel for centripetal force, is shown in Fig. 1. This demonstration is fun to operate, educational, and not overly difficult to construct. The main component is the back part of a ten-speed bicycle.

Two lead-filled carts are free to roll on tracks that have been mounted to the rear wheel of the ten-speed bicycle. The wheel is turned by using the foot crank and hub mechanism from the same

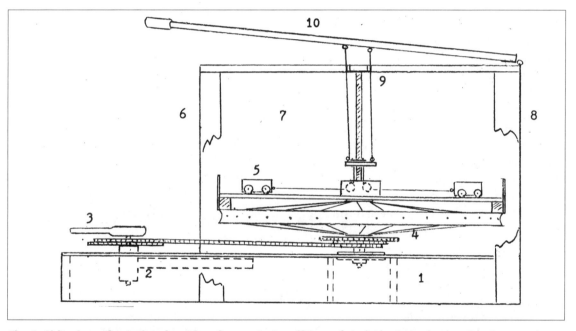

Fig. 1. **Side view of rotational motion demonstrator.** *(l)* Base of stock l by 4 pine lumber. Base is covered with plywood to form a platform approximately 120 by 75 cm. *(2)* Bicycle crank hub with short lengths of frame attached. Clamp the lengths of frame to the base. *(3)* Crank has been shortened. Foot pedal has been removed. Adding stops to prevent the crank from turning more than 180° is recommended. This modification discourages high-speed operation of the device. *(4)* Ten-speed rear wheel. Use the lowest gear ratio. An 8.2-cm-wide by 0.95-cm-thick piece of plywood is mounted across one diameter of the wheel to hold the track for the carts. *(5)* Carts are made of 10-cm lengths of 5.1-cm by 5.1-cm tubular steel. Pour molten lead into the steel forms. Wheels are made of sliding glass door rollers approximately 3.8 cm in diameter. Metal wheels are better than nylon. These wheels are available at hardware stores for about $4 per pair. Wheels are mounted on the carts with 0.64-cm x 3.8-cm lag screws. Drill 0.64-cm holes through the steel jacket of the cart, then a 0.3-cm pilot hole into the lead. The lag screws will screw easily into the lead. Accurate placement of the holes is essential so that all four wheels will touch a flat surface at the same time: use a drill press. The carts ride on two parallel aluminum tracks. Each track is a channel 1.3 cm wide by 0.8 cm deep and of a length equal to the diameter of the bicycle wheel you choose to use. *(6)* Corner pieces are 3.8-cm by 3.8-cm aluminum angles. I placed 1.6-cm by 3.0-cm pine strips behind these corner pieces to reinforce the structure as well as to provide material to hold the acrylic windows in place. Short screws go through the aluminum, through the acrylic, and into the wood. *(7)* Acrylic windows on three sides of the apparatus. *(8)* The back of the apparatus is made of 0.95-cm-thick plywood. *(9)* Anti-twist cable assembly and wheel stabilizer (Fig. 2). *(10)* Pine board lifting handle.

Phys. Teach. **26,** 187-188 (March 1988)

bicycle. A lifting handle is provided to pull the carts to the center of the rotating wheel. The centripetal force required to hold the carts in a particular position can be experienced qualitatively. When the carts are moved to different positions along the radius of the rotating wheel, changes in the rotational velocity of the system can be observed qualitatively.

Construction Details

Figs. 1 and 2, along with comments in the keys to the figures, describe the apparatus in sufficient detail. Dimensions are not critical. Changes can be made to use materials that may be on hand.

Comments

This exhibit was specifically designed for the Frank Oppenheimer Memorial Exhibit and can be used in a corridor setting without supervision. A similar model, constructed from the front wheel of the bicycle, can be used in the laboratory under the supervision of an instructor. In this model, the bicycle wheel is spun by hand. The carts are pulled to the center with high-strength nylon cord. The vertical steel flat and related mechanism shown in Fig. 2 is not required. The cords, after passing through the center pulleys, are pulled upward. The cords will entwine, but performance will not be affected during the course of a brief laboratory trial. A Newton scale can be used to pull upward on the cords so that the forces involved can be approximated. A curved acrylic transparent strip can be attached to the outer circumference of the bike wheel. Pieces of black tape placed on the acrylic strip form a "picket fence" that will enable accurate photo cell timing of the action of trial runs. Using this data, quantitative relationships can be determined.

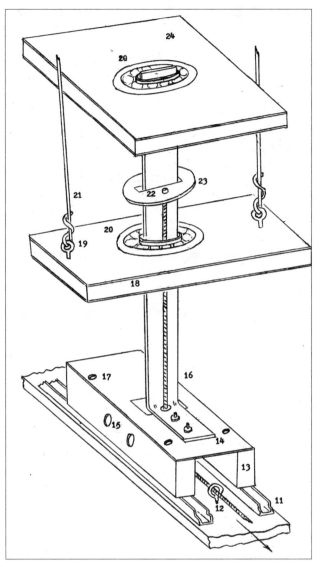

Fig. 2. No-tangle lift mechanism. *(11)* Aluminum channel 1.3 cm wide by 0.8 cm deep (Handi Metal # HM-1285 EA). *(12)* Bicycle brake cable passes through screw-eye guide. *(13)* Pine block pulley housing and vertical mechanism support. *(14)* Sheet aluminum cover. *(15)* Bolts to hold inside pulleys. Pulleys should be wide with deep grooves. *(16)* Vertical steel flat approximately 1.2-1.8 cm wide by 0.3 cm thick. *(17)* Bolts pass through pulley housing block, track, and track support board. *(18)* Plywood, the same thickness as the ball bearing, sandwiched between sheet aluminum. *(19)* Eyebolt. *(20)* Machine ball bearing with center bore large enough to accommodate vertical flat. *(21)* Coat hanger wire, attached at upper end to eyebolts in the lifting handle. *(22)* The small hole in each side of this bracket is large enough to accommodate a bicycle brake cable but too small to allow the cable end knob to pass. *(23)* Steel cable-end bracket rotates on ball bearing. Use a drill, chisel, and file to make the slot to fit the vertical flat. *(24)* Plywood between sheet aluminum sandwiches ball bearing in a fixed position. The sandwich is secured to pine cross pieces in the top structure. Open spaces in the top were covered with acrylic.

Animated Displays III: Mechanical Puzzles

Paul Chagnon, University of Notre Dame, Notre Dame, IN 46556

Elementary demonstrations can be made to work reliably without a human operator, and so can be made available on demand as in a display case. Such animated displays fall between "hands-on" experience and classroom presentation.

In an earlier article[1] I outlined some general ideas about animated displays. Here I describe an exhibit containing four quite elementary demonstrations relating to center of gravity and to rotational equilibrium: the stack of bricks (not animated), the double cone, the spool roller, and the platform (or Roberval) balance. They are presented as paradoxes or puzzles.

None of these displays is new in concept. The first surely was known in antiquity. The others were all described exactly by Sutton[2] and at least two of them are much older than his compilation. Even the apparatus itself, on which each display is based, is of indeterminate age. It is the animation that is novel, and that is the main subject. Some of the animation is itself elementary while some proved to be more challenging. Of course no vestige of any difficulties encountered must be evident to the viewer. Each mechanism must substitute in a natural or transparent way for the human agent.

Stack of Bricks

This is an eye-catcher that is not animated. It ties in well with the other displays and rounds out the whole exhibit. The idea is sometimes presented as a problem in textbooks[3] in a form something like the following. A number of identical uniform rectangular solids (bricks) is to be stacked up so that the maximum possible offset is achieved without the stack tipping over. As a particular goal we may require that the top brick not overlay the bottom one, i.e., that the sum of the offsets ex-

Fig. 1. The plumb bob shows that there is plenty of clearance between the top and bottom bricks in this stack of seven.

ceeds the length of one brick, and ask for the minimum number of bricks needed.

The solution of the idealized problem is straightforward. For each brick, the center of gravity of all the bricks above it is to be located directly above its edge. If the bricks be enumerated from the top down, each offset then equals half the length of a brick, multiplied by (1, 1/2, 1/3,...), that is the harmonic series. Since the sequence of partial sums diverges, any required offset can be achieved. Only four terms (overhanging bricks) are needed for the stated case, plus the bottom brick, making five. To have reasonable stability and to allow for flaws, at least six real bricks should be used, and seven if it is to be quite evident that the top brick completely overhangs the bottom one (Fig. 1).

For best results, select bricks that have flat tops and bottoms with square corners. Rounded corners make it impossible to approach the ideal. Of course, we could use machined metal or wooden blocks, but to do so would raise people's suspicions that they are cemented to-

Phys. Teach. **31**, 32-37 (Jan. 1993)

Fig. 2. The double cone. At this point the cam, which turns counterclockwise, has been holding up the left end of the apparatus. The double cone has rolled to its starting position at the narrow "lower" end of the rails. In a moment the board will drop to the level position and the double cone will roll up the rails.

gether. It seems advisable to stick to (no pun intended) common brick, where the absence of mortar suggests the absence of fraud.

Two stacks like the one in Fig. 1, face to face, form a stable arch. The application to primitive architecture, when mortar was unreliable, is self-explanatory.

Double Cone

Is there anyone who was not bemused upon seeing, for the first time, the double cone gravitating to the higher end of its inclined rails?

Fig. 3. On each side of this platform balance, two small pans are supported by a rigid frame about 0.1 m square. At the moment it was photographed, the righthand weight rested on the inner pan while the left weight was being carried by its crank from pan to pan. The balance goes level whenever both weights rest on pans, in any combination.

That this paradox has been around for a long time is exemplified by a detailed explanation with drawings, to be found in an 1867 textbook,[4] which suggests that it was not new even then.

Animating this device consists mainly of returning the double cone to the narrow "lower" end of the rails from time to time. We set the rails on a plywood rectangle bearing two pairs of padded dowel posts placed so as to stop the cone at each end of its travel (Fig. 2). This is hinged, at the narrow end of the rails, to a similar, fixed plywood base. The posts at the wide end, and one screw at the narrow end, serve to hold the rail assembly in place. A small timing motor, driving a wooden cam, raises one end of the top plywood periodically, and the cone rolls to the narrow end of the rails. When the cam drops the apparatus to a level position, the cone rolls in its normal "paradoxical" direction.

The construction is evident in Fig. 2. The cam makes one revolution in 15 s. For half this period, the base remains level. Then the wide end of the rails is raised about 25 mm and held at that height while the cone returns to the narrow end. Only about 3 s are required for each motion of the cone, so there is a few seconds' pause at each end. To keep the cone in constant motion would probably be distracting.

After this device was first incorporated into a display, it happened a few times that the cone would be found lying between the rails at the wide end. A possible explanation is based on the observation that when the cone reaches the

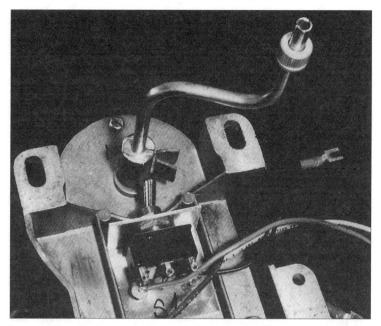

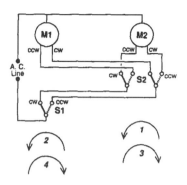

Fig. 5. Electrical diagram for the platform balance actuator. M1 and M2 are reversible ac gearhead motors that can trip switches S1 and S2 respectively, as in the preceding figure. As shown, power is routed to the counterclockwise (ccw) input of M2. At the end of almost one revolution, M2 will throw S2 to the ccw position, M1 will run ccw, and so on. The curved arrows indicate the cycle of actions that results.

Fig. 4. This crank, from the platform balance actuator, is driven by a motor that, in this case, would be turning slowly clockwise. Soon the cam attached to its shaft will throw the toggle switch so that the other motor runs. When power is restored to this motor, it will turn counterclockwise. A cycle of four such operations ensues.

wide-end bumpers it is spinning and that rotation is stopped rather abruptly by the frictional torque exerted on it. It seems conceivable that, on occasion, when the cone comes along the rails crooked, this frictional torque turns the cone's axis still more, enough for it to fall between the rails. When bits of ordinary transparent tape were put over the padding on the bumpers, the cone "spun down" noticeably more slowly, indicating less torque, and indeed the problem disappeared until the tape eventually wore out.

Designing the cam so that the rails drop abruptly into place solved another problem, the occasional refusal of the cone to roll at all, perhaps due to specks of dust or irregularities in the wood. The slight jar gets the cone moving without fail.

Platform, or Roberval, Balance

The common platform balance is attributed to the French mathematician Gilles de Roberval (1602-1675). Its principal feature is that the balance condition is independent of the position of the load on the platform or pan. This is certainly at odds with the simple balance of Archimedes, and so it is sometimes construed as a paradox. The mystery is perhaps enhanced by the custom of enclosing the relevant linkage inside the base of commercial balances. Advice on the construction of a demonstration model is to be found in recent articles[5] that also explain the principle.

Our equal-arm demonstration platform balance has two little pans on each side, about 0.1 m apart (Fig. 3). Since they are rigidly connected, this is purely to emphasize the main point; moving a weight from one pan to the other (on the same side of the balance) dramatizes its change in position. Two equal weights, of about 0.5 kg mass, can be placed in four possible arrangements, in any of which the system balances. A fully convincing display requires the four positions to be demonstrated in turn, that is, each of the weights must be moved between each of its pans. This is much more effective than an earlier version of this display in which only one weight moved, and which therefore did not carry the balance through its full range of motion. As usual, the

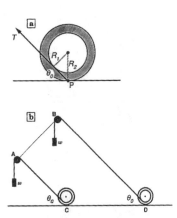

Fig. 6.(a) Tension *T* Is applied to a cord wrapped around the drum or spool. If the cord makes a particular angle θ_0 with the horizontal, there is no torque about point P, the point of contact between the roller and the horizontal floor. (b) When the pulley supporting weight *w* moves from A to B, the equilibrium position of the spool roller follows from C to D, keeping the same angle θ_0. If AB is perpendicular to the cord, just as much extra cord unrolls as is needed.

Fig. 7. The roller, on its hardwood board about 1.5 m long overall, is seen in its left equilibrium position. The actuator on the ring stand can move the pulley and weight on a diagonal up and to the right, to the position it has in the photograph of the whole display case in Fig. 9.

operating mechanism must be easily distinguished from the display, and must clearly not influence the result.

To accomplish this we mounted two reversible gearhead motors behind a panel standing behind the balance, and well above the weights to be moved. Each motor turns a crank back and forth through just less than a full revolution. The crank circle diameter equals the horizontal distance to be traveled. A very limp cord connects the end of each crank to one of the weights (Fig. 3). In due time, each crank starts from nearly its bottom-center position, lifts up its weight, carries it across and lowers it onto the other pan, after which the cord goes slack and the motor stops in a position conjugate to its starting point. For this to work well it is necessary to restrict the vertical motion of the balance somewhat.

First one motor operates, then the other, then each in turn repeats in the opposite direction. This is quite easily managed. Just as each crank approaches its resting position, a cam on its shaft flips an ordinary toggle switch (Fig. 4) that routes power to the other motor and simultaneously sets up its own motor for the opposite rotation when its turn comes again. All of the necessary connections, and the sequence of four motions that result, are shown in Fig. 5. Enough delay results from the over travel of the cranks for the equilibrium to be witnessed each time before it is disturbed again.

Whenever a weight is moved, it swings as a pendulum while in transit, so its exact landing place is quite unpredictable, sometimes almost missing the target pan entirely. This makes the display's action seem even more "natural" and helps to allay suspicion that the result is a special case, or is contrived.

Rolling Spool, or Underslung Roller

A cord is wrapped around the core of a spool, of radius R_1, the radius of whose flanges is R_2, as in Fig. 6a. There is a certain angle $\theta_0 = \cos^{-1}(R_1/R_2)$ at which the line of action of a ten-

Interactive Physics Demonstrations

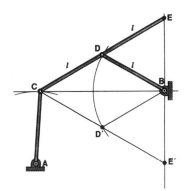

Fig. 8. An adaptation of Watt's linkage, by which point E (carrying the pulley, in our case) is constrained to follow a very nearly straight path through B and E', as explained in the text. Of course, in the real assembly the different links are not all in the same plane. A crank arm, not shown here, attached at D, completes the conversion between circular and reciprocating linear motion. This diagram, if rotated approximately 135°, corresponds to the linkage as seen in the photographs.

Fig. 9. For the purpose of this photograph of the whole exhibit, all of the lights and signs were turned on at the same time. Clockwise from the lower left: the stack of bricks, the double cone (on the shelf), the actuator for the spool roller, the Roberval balance, and the spool roller itself. All three moving displays are at positions different from their individual photographs on preceding pages. At the center is another Illuminated sign inviting the viewer to touch the operating button fastened to the window just below the sign. The shelf at eye level across the display case is barely deep enough to hold its two displays. The plane of the spool roller display lies just behind this shelf. Supplementary lighting for individual displays is concealed beneath the shelf and at the top of the case.

sion force T applied to the cord passes through the point of contact P between the spool and the floor. If the roller is on a horizontal surface, its weight passes through P, as does the contact force, so there is no torque about P and the roller is in rotational equilibrium (if it is in translational equilibrium). If the angle of the tension (or the cord) is greater or less than θ_0, the net torque clockwise or counterclockwise, respectively, will make the roller accelerate to the right or left. Therein lies the seeming paradox, that a pull, say to the left, can produce motion to the right.

If the cord is pulled from a fixed point, rather than a fixed angle, the roller oscillates around, and eventually settles at, the position for which the equilibrium angle θ_0 obtains. In our animated demonstration, tension is provided by a small weight w hanging from a pulley (Fig. 6b). The pulley translates along line AB in the figure, perpendicular to the equilib-

rium angle of the cord. The roller's equilibrium position moves back and forth between points C and D. The roller overshoots these positions and oscillates a bit around each of them.

There are specific reasons for moving the pulley along a line perpendicular to the equilibrium angle. The foremost is to avoid fostering any misconception that a change in the magnitude of the tension occurs and is responsible for the roller's motion ("You're pushing on the string"). The other is that the length of cord unrolled from the spool as it rolls from C to D is exactly equal to the required increase $\overline{BD}-\overline{AC}$, independent of the value of θ_0. That implies that the weight w need not move relative to the pulley, except to accommodate the oscillations around equilibrium. This also reinforces the correct notion that the magnitude of the tension remains nearly constant.

In our display (Fig. 7), the roller is a cast aluminum alloy spool originally used for ship-

Appendix I. Illuminated Signs

Figure 10 is a sketch of an easy-to-make illuminated holder for a standard-size page of text. The key is to make a sandwich consisting of a diffuser, the text (in large type) on an overhead transparency or on thin paper, and a colored gelatin filter. Diffusing material can be had cheaply at building-supply houses, but if available, white Plexiglas made for the purpose is superior. Covering the text with a colored filter makes it less noticeable under normal illumination but draws attention when the lamp behind it is turned on. An ordinary 25- or 40-W lamp in a basemounting socket is satisfactory. The bottom of the sandwich fits into a groove sawed into the wooden base, and its top rests on a dowel rail supported by thin strips of wood. Our signs have open sides, but metal sides might be desirable. A half-size version of the sign uses small candelabra-based lamps and omits the upper support.

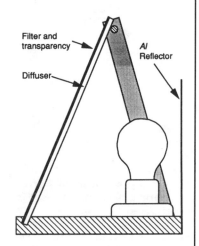

Fig. 10. Side view of an illuminated sign holder.

ping wire, with R_2 = 80 mm, $R_1 \approx$ 57 mm, and a mass of 0.9 kg. Small flanges constrain the cord to the center of the spool. Distance $\overline{AB}$ = 0.4 m, and since $\theta_0 \approx 45°$, distance $\overline{CD} \approx 0.55$ m. Since the maximum amplitude of oscillation is about equal to $\overline{CD}$, the track on which the roller travels might need to be thrice $\overline{CD}$ in length. In practice, the oscillations rarely approach such an amplitude. The actual track has a free length of about 2.2 times $\overline{CD}$ with small wedges at the ends to deal with the occasional large excursion.

How to convert the unidirectional rotation of a motor to the desired reciprocating straight-line motion, with only a rudimentary mechanism? That is just the inverse of the problem faced by early steam-engine designers, so we adopted a linkage devised by James Watt. In Fig. 8, points A and B are fixed. Lengths $\overline{BD}$, $\overline{CD}$, and $\overline{DE}$ are equal. Elementary geometry shows that if C were constrained to the horizontal line, then E would move along a vertical straight line through B to E'. Actually, C moves on a circle of large radius, but through a relatively small arc. Consequently the end of the "walking beam" CDE travels nearly straight. The amount of deviation depends on the length of link $\overline{AC}$ and the length of stroke

$\overline{EE}'$ relative to the modulus $\overline{BD}$. For compactness, we chose $\overline{AC}$ = ($\overline{BD}$, etc.) = 0.15 m and $\overline{EE}'$ = 0.4 m, with barely perceptible deviation at the ends of the travel. (Watt's linkage approximates straight-line motion with only three links. True straight-line linkages with seven or more links may be found in reference books.[6])

A motor with a crank and connecting arm attached to D or to some other convenient point completes the driving mechanism for this display (Fig. 7). In the present application, the whole is rotated through the required angle, and the pulley in Fig. 6b is attached at end E of the walking beam. It is important to stop the motion of the pulley at each end of its travel for about 10 s while the roller's oscillation settles. The same electrical circuit used in other displays[7] will do the job. Only one microswitch is required, since arm AC takes up the same position as can be seen in Fig. 8, at both extremes of the motion.

Successful animation of the roller requires dealing with the related problems of guidance and slippage. Both of these could be eliminated with some kind of rack-and-pinion arrangement, which would seem too contrived and artificial for this application. Since the roller cannot be expected to travel in a perfectly repro-ducible path, some form of "course correction" has to occur at times. Whenever this happens, one flange or the other must slip so that a bit of cord unwinds; with use, weight w gradually descends, and eventually the cord must be rewound. It appears that other slippage results from minute bumps in the surfaces making rolling contact. Guidance requires some sliding friction; the more friction, the greater weight w must be to overcome it, and the more of this incidental slippage occurs. We consider it acceptable to have to rewind the cord not more than once a week, i.e., each few hundred minutes of operation, and were able to achieve this by minimizing the amount of guidance re-

---

Appendix II. Text for the Displays

• *The Stack-of-Bricks Paradox*

Notice that—the bricks are not fastened together in any way. The top brick completely overhangs the bottom one. Yet the stack does not tip over!

Solution: Suppose that the bricks are numbered from the top down. Then the center of gravity of brick #1 must be placed somewhere over brick #2. The combined center of gravity of #1 and #2 must be somewhere over brick #3, and so on indefinitely. Given enough bricks, there is no limit in principle to how far over the top brick can go. After the first few bricks, the maximum distance increases only very slowly. In olden times arches — the basis of architecture — could be made in this way without mortar.

• *The Double-Cone Paradox*

Notice that—the cone rolls toward the higher end of the inclined track!

Solution: As the track gets wider, the axis of the cone, and thus its center of gravity, actually gets lower as the cone moves toward the "higher" end.

• *The Platform Balance*

Notice that—(1) when a weight is moved from one pan to the other, the system balances just the same. The distance from the center doesn't seem to matter! (2) Although the weights are well above the pivot, the balance doesn't tip all the way to one side or another like a seesaw, but comes to stable equilibrium!

Solutions: (1) This is not a simple lever. Torques around the upper pivot include one due to the horizontal force in the lower arm. Since the outer frame must itself be in rotational equilibrium, this must exactly compensate the extra torque produced when the weight is moved farther out. (2) The pivot at the center of the horizontal arms is higher than those at the ends. This causes the center of gravity to move slightly to the left when the arm turns clockwise, and vice versa.

Paradoxical or not, this is how all practical platform balances have to be made, since the exact position of the weight on the platform *must* not matter.

• *The Spool Roller Paradox*

Notice that—the string is always pulling to the left, yet this sometimes makes the roller move to the right!

Solution: Consider the roller to be turning about the point where it touches the table (this sign includes a sketch like the one in Fig. 6a). If the line of the string passes exactly through this point, the tension force produces no torque about it, and the roller is stable. If the angle of the string is increased or decreased a little, this tension tends to turn the roller clockwise or counterclockwise, respectively.

---

quired and the associated sliding friction.

We machined the periphery of the spool's flanges empirically so as to make it roll as straight as possible on a long flat floor. (One attempt to use rubber tires was decidedly unsatisfactory, but it might be worth trying again.) The track is a hardwood board, sanded and sealed but unvarnished. A single guide rail about 6 mm high and half as wide as the roller runs down the center of the board. The edges of the rail, where lateral contact occurs, are slanted about 10° and covered with polypropylene tape. As a result, the roller appears to be unencumbered, there is little drag when it touches the rail, and as for weight w, a mass of 0.1 kg is more than sufficient to assure that the roller never sticks in place. The actuator is placed high in the display case so that the weight can fall more than 1 m before the cord must be rewound, as it turns out, once or twice a month.

Presentation

The four displays are accommodated without crowding by arranging the roller behind the other three, which require but little depth. Each of the four is accompanied by its illuminated sign (see Appendix I). When one of them is selected, its actuator (except for the stack of bricks), its sign, and where applicable its individual lighting, are turned on, as is general lighting of the display case. While independent pushbuttons could be used, it is convenient to present the displays in rotation when the same button is activated, as suggested in Ref. 1, on the idea that the viewer's attention ought to be focused on only one display at a time for at least 30 s. If the proximity-sensitive button is

not touched at all for about three minutes, the whole exhibit shuts down. There remains enough exterior lighting for passersby to notice the exhibit, as well as one illuminated sign directing them to operate the button. Each activation of the button also advances an electrical counter that helps to gauge how much attention the exhibit is receiving.

Text for each display is listed in Appendix II. In this case, since the exhibit is presented as a collection of puzzles, the format departs somewhat from the usual "What is going on...." Rather, a "solution" is offered. These are rather terse so that large print can be used. In some cases only a hint is given to steer the viewer's thinking in the right direction.

References

1. P.R. Chagnon, "Animated displays I: Coupled mechanical oscillators," *Phys. Teach.* **30**, 275 (1992).

2. R.M. Sutton, *Demonstration Experiments in Physics* (McGraw-Hill, New York, 1938), pp. 23, 26, and 29.

3. R. Resnick, D. Halliday, and K.S. Krane, *Physics*, 4th ed. (Wiley, New York, 1992), p. 313, problem 37; and earlier editions.

4. P.A. Daguin, *Traite de Physique*, 3rd ed. (Edouard Privat, Toulouse, 1867), Vol. I, p. 126.

5. H. Richard Crane, "How things work," *Phys. Teach.* **29**, 593 (1991); P.R. Chagnon, "The Roberval balance," *Phys. Teach.* **30**, 238 (1992).

6. G.D. Hiscox, *Mechanical Appliances and Novelties of Construction* (Henley New York, 1927), p. 245.

7. P.R. Chagnon, "Animated displays II: Multiple reflections," *Phys. Teach.* **30**, 488 (1992).

Ice and Balls

Carol L. Miles, University of Canterbury, Department of Physics, Christchurch 1, New Zealand

Corridor demonstrations are interesting to both students and "casual" passers-by. They should ideally be simple enough to understand in a single glance, yet interesting enough to merit a second look.

"Ice and Balls" is an easy demonstration to set up and one that arouses interest; people will often return for a second look. The photos just about tell the whole story. At the top is a "spot" type of clear heat lamp, with a built-in reflector. It's rated at 272 W, but the exact value is not critical.

In the center of Fig. 1 is shown a block of ice with two balls on its surface. Fig. 2 shows the result about two hours later. The black aluminum ball has sunk into the ice more than the

Fig. 1. Above, a block of ice with two balls on its surface.

Fig. 2. Right, the results, about two hours later.

Phys. Teach. **26**, 536-537 (Nov. 1988)

one with the reflective finish.

Many physical concepts can be referred to in this demonstration. For example: the greater absorption of energy by a black body (and re-radiation, too, although that does not show up here); the force of gravity pressing the balls in contact with the ice; the rate of melting, partially determined by the wattage of the balls; and so forth.

To make this demonstration as effective as possible, several points should be mentioned:

1. The balls should be good conductors. That is, glass won't do. These balls are of aluminum, one black anodized and the other clear anodized. They are about 20 mm in diameter.

2. The coatings should be black in the IR and good conductors. Thus, painting metal balls with white and black paint is not satisfactory. Even quite white paints are strong absorbers in the IR, which is why home heating radiators are often effectively painted with aluminum paint. Anodized surfaces (basically, Al_2O_3 is sapphire, and very thin) are good. Of course, gold plating on the bright sphere would be better, but just clear anodize is good enough. It's difficult to get a good, strongly adherent black surface on copper. Blued-steel and chromed-steel balls might work, but these have not been tried. Note too that the ice is propped up on wood (poor thermal conductor) blocks.

3. Be sure that the bottom tray is large enough!

Finally, I remember hearing a story which caused me to set up this experiment. The Eskimos of British Columbia and the Yukon used this technique to "drill holes" in the ice for fishing. Only, for the black metal ball they substituted dog dung!

Vibrations and Waves

Simple Vibrating Systems

Thomas D. Rossing, Department of Physics, Northern Illinois University, DeKalb, IL 60115

This demonstration was selected as one of the "favorites" in the Frank OppenheimerMemorial Exhibit, which was held January 27-30, 1987, at the Exploratorium, San Francisco.

Anyone who has taken a mechanics course knows that a mass suspended from a spring having a spring constant K will oscillate with a frequency $f = (K/m)^{1/2}/2\pi$. A little intuition will show that if a second mass of the same size is added, the frequency becomes $f = (K/2m)^{1/2}/2\pi$. Not quite so obvious is the effect of adding a second spring. It depends, of course, on whether the two springs are connected in series or in parallel.

If a second spring is added in "parallel," as in Fig. 1(c), a given displacement x of the mass results in twice the restoring force with one spring, and so the frequency of oscillation increases by $(2)^{1/2}$. If the springs are connected in "series," however, as in Fig. 1(d), a displacement x only stretches each spring by x/2, so the restoring force is halved, and the oscillation frequency is $1/(2)^{1/2}$ as great as before. Continuing the same line of reasoning leads to the correct frequencies for the two-mass/ two spring configurations in Fig. 1(e) and 1(f).

Phys. Teach. **26**, 50-51 (Jan. 1988)

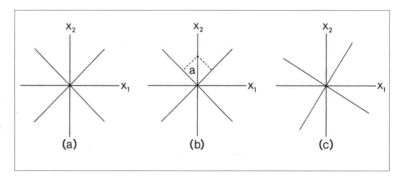

Fig. 1. Simple mass/spring vibrating systems. Systems a–f have single modes with frequencies: a) $(K/m)^{1/2}/2\pi$; b) $(K/2m)^{1/2}/2\pi$; c) $(2K/m)^{1/2}/2\pi$; d) $(K/2m)^{1/2}/2\pi$; e) $(K/4m)^{1/2}/2\pi$; f) $(K/m)^{1/2}/2\pi$. Systems g and h each have two normal modes with frequencies: g) $0.62\ (K/m)^{1/2}/2\pi$ and $1.62\ (K/m)^{1/2}/2\pi$; h) $(K/m)^{1/2}/2\pi$ and $(3K/m)^{1/2}/2\pi$.

Fig. 2. Graphical representation of normal modes on graphs of x_2 vs. x_1. a) System illustrated in Fig. 1(h) has normal modes that can be represented by two lines: $x_2 = x_1$ and $x_2 = -x_1$. b) Giving mass 2 an initial displacement $x_2 = a$ excites the system in both modes with equal amplitude $a/(2)^{1/2}$. c) System illustrated in Fig. 1(g) has normal modes represented by lines: $x_2 = 1.618\ x_1$ and $x_2 = -0.618\ x_1$.

The configuration in Fig. 1(g) has two normal modes of vibration. In the mode of lower frequency [$f_1 = 0.62\ (K/m)^{1/2}/2\pi$], the two masses move in the same direction; in the mode of higher frequency [$f_2 = 1.62$ $(K/m)^{1/2}/2\pi$], the masses move in opposite directions. The more familiar configuration in Fig. 1(h) has frequencies $f_1 = (K/m)^{1/2}/2\pi$ and $f_2 = (3K/m)^{1/2}/2\pi$.

Because of the symmetry it is considerably easier to excite the modes in 1(h) than in 1(g). Thus, this is probably the better configuration for an interactive corridor experiment. Exciting the higher mode in 1(g) takes some patience; the upper mass should be given an initial amplitude that is about 60% greater than the lower one.

An interesting way to represent the normal modes of a two-mode system such as 1(g) or 1(h) is by making a graph of x_2 vs x_1 where x_2 and x_1 are the displacements of the two masses from equilibrium. For the system in 1(h), such a graph results in two straight lines: $x_2 = x_1$ and $x_2 = -x_1$, as shown in Fig. 2(a). The system can be made to oscillate along either path (i.e., in either normal mode) independently of the other. If we give an initial displacement $x_2 = a$ to mass 2 and none to mass 1, we would excite both modes with amplitudes represented by the projections of point $x_2 = a$ on the two curves, as shown in Fig. 2(b). Do not forget that the frequencies of the modes differ by some 73%, however, so the path will not be along the $x_1 = 0$ axis (i.e., mass 1 quickly begins to oscillate, also).

For the system in 1(g), the two normal modes are represented by the perpendicular lines: $x_2 = 1.618\ x_1$ and $x_2 = -0.618\ x_1$, as shown in Fig. 2(c).

Designing the Corridor Apparatus

The simple apparatus shown in Fig. 3, which was displayed at the Frank Oppenheimer Memorial Exhibit at The Exploratorium, was designed to be the basis of a homework problem for students in my Acoustics and Vibration class. Residing in an open laboratory, in more of a museum-like environment, it does not have to be quite as rugged as apparatus for a corridor experiment. I can only speculate

Fig. 3. Richard Peterson (Bethel College), organizer of the Oppenheimer Memorial Exhibit at The Exploratorium, measures the frequency of configuration 1(f).

how best to design similar apparatus for open-corridor use.

For corridor use, the most important thing is to select rugged springs. A spring constant in the range of 60 to 100 N/m makes it convenient to use ordinary 1-kg masses. Lengths of the pigtails on the springs and/or the connecting links may have to be adjusted to minimize interaction with pendulum modes. (For classroom demonstration use, on the other hand, such interactions add interest).

For corridor use, it is probably desirable to divide the apparatus into two parts. One part would be used to study the single-mode systems in Fig. 1(a)–(f), and the other part would have either of the two-mass configurations in 1(g) or 1(h) permanently mounted. In this part, it might be wise to protect at least the upper spring from overstretching by inserting a strong cord of the right length inside the spring.

The Sand Pendulum

Joe Pizzo, Department of Physics, Lamar University, Beaumont, TX 77710

The sand pendulum is an exhibit that is sure to bring out the playfulness and delight the imagination of any participant. The purpose of this exhibit is to provide a graphic illustration of the interplay between two simple harmonic motions, with different frequencies, at right angles to each other. The design and construction of the sand pendulum, pictured in Fig. 1, will be discussed here in terms of four basic components: the pendulum itself, the sandbox, the "writing tablet," and the suspension system.

The Pendulum

The pendulum itself consists of a heavy metal funnel, with a small outlet, suspended from two points on a horizontal bar by two cords, each approximately 1.5 m long. A sliding clip holds the cords together at any desired distance from the suspension bar (see Fig. 2). Graphics encourage the user of this exhibit to slide the clip to different positions, thereby varying the period of the oscillation parallel to the suspension bar.

The funnels, cords, and clip may be obtained for under $25 from the Sargent-Welch Scientific Company.[1] We have experimented with various homemade funnels but are much more satisfied with the commercial version.

The Sandbox

The sandbox is nothing more than a large box, made with a plywood bottom and sides made from 1 by 8's, elevated to a convenient height by a sturdy, well-braced stand made from 2 by 4's. The finished assembly is shown in Fig. 1.

The sand, which must be fine grained and dry, can be obtained from either a toy store or a painting contractor who uses "blasting sand."

Phys. Teach. **25**, 240-241 (April 1987)

Fig. 1. The sand pendulum.

We provide a small sugar scoop to transfer sand into the funnel.

The Writing Tablet

A small platform is constructed from a piece of plywood and 1 by 4's. The length and width of the platform should each be about 100 mm shorter than the length and width of the sandbox. The platform is placed in the center of the sandbox, and then the sand is poured into the space between the platform and the sides of the sandbox (Fig. 2). A black cloth, placed on the platform, provides a good contrast for the light-colored sand (Fig. 3). The patterns created by the sand pendulum can be erased simply by lifting one side of the cloth and dumping the sand back into the tray.

The Suspension System

Two tall aluminum rods are firmly attached in *diagonally* opposite corners of the sandbox (Fig. 1). A wooden bar, with a hole in each end, is slipped over the aluminum rods and held at the top by friction (and clamps for insurance). The two strings of the pendulum are attached to screw eyes in the wooden crossbar.

One of the unique features of our sand pendulum is the diagonal placement of the suspension bar. This invariably ensures a Lissajous pattern with equal amplitudes in both directions, since most users have a natural tendency to activate the pendulum by pulling it toward themselves while standing in front of the apparatus.

Comments

We find it unnecessary to give instructions for filling the funnel, activating the pendulum, and erasing the pattern, since the design of the apparatus makes these operations self-evident.

Our graphics simply point out that the pendulum will simultaneously swing (with different frequencies) in two directions and that the frequencies depend on the "length of the swing" in each direction. Moreover, we point out that the pattern will depend on the ratio of these frequencies and can be changed by mov-

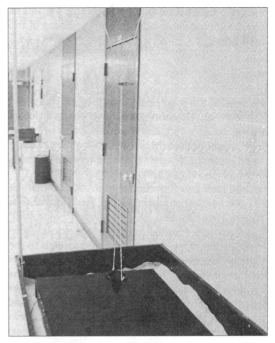

Fig. 2. A view of the sand pendulum, showing a clothespin used as a sliding clip.

ing the sliding clip to change the "length of swing" parallel to the bar.

If you plan to place a sand pendulum in your hallway, you must be prepared to tolerate the occasional silly message left by some "wit" who works the pendulum by hand as a writing instrument.

Reference

1. Sargent-Welch Scientific Company, 7300 North Linder Ave., P.O. Box 1026, Skokie, IL 60077. (The pendulum described is listed on p. 492 of the 1986-87 catalog.)

Fig. 3. A Lissajous pattern "written" in sand on the black cloth.

Animated Displays: Coupled Mechanical Oscillators

Paul Chagnon, Physics Department, University of Notre Dame, Notre Dame, IN 46556

There are circumstances, such as those relating to lack of space, lack of building security, or delicacy of equipment, that may make interactive corridor displays impractical in a given case. Still, displays with action attract much more attention and can make their points more effectively than purely static ones. To fill the gap, a number of sets of animated, though not interactive, displays have been developed suitable for a display case measuring approximately 2 m wide and 0.5 m deep. Each set combines several simple, usually fairly standard, demonstrations having a common theme. Depending on the particular case, the demonstration may run continuously, be turned on by a motion detector sensing the presence of viewers, or be activated by one or more viewer-operated pushbuttons. Each "show" remains in the display case for a few months; the animated displays are interspersed with slide shows, videos, and occasionally static displays, so the same presentation is not repeated more than once every three or four years.

We describe here a set of displays on the theme of coupled mechanical oscillators. The displays (Fig. 1) encompass three common demonstrations: a coupled pair of identical pendulums, a multiple-pendulum resonance demonstration, and a Wilberforce coupled oscillator.

Coupled oscillators are not ordinarily encountered by students until an intermediate

Phys. Teach. **30**, 275-279 (May 1992)

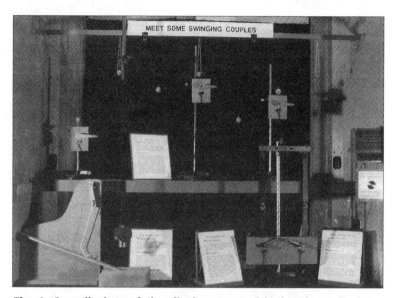

Fig. 1. Overall view of the display case, with the three displays, several signs, some illuminated, and a proximity-sensitive "pushbutton" with its own signage at the far right.

mechanics or circuit analysis course, and then the subject is likely to come across as formal mathematical analysis of phenomena with which the students have little or no acquaintance. On the other hand, concrete examples are fascinating to watch, and qualitative explanations can be understood by people in introductory courses. Of course the applications in quantum mechanics are all-important.

General Guidelines

Any animated display should make a clear distinction between the demonstration itself and the activating mechanism that substitutes for a human operator. To this end, in these displays there is no physical connection between each oscillator and its actuator, except while the actuator is operating. Each actuator is similar in operation to a finger or hand, and in most cases is supported independently of the oscillators, e.g., on a separate ring stand and

Fig. 2. One of the simple-pendulum actuators (turning counterclockwise) about to release its pendulum.

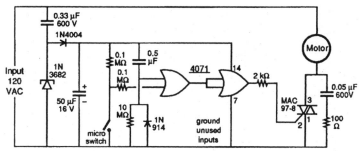

Fig. 3. Diagram of the circuit that allows one actuator to execute one revolution of the output shaft when power is applied for an indefinite period. *Caution:* this circuit is not isolated from the power line. An illuminated sign may be connected in parallel with the input, so that it remains lit after the motor stops.

painted in a dull neutral color, while the working parts of the oscillators are in bright colors. An earlier policy of concealing the working of the actuators has been abandoned, since the working parts are of particular interest to staff and advanced and graduate physics students.

Each display should present enough action to sustain the interest of the average passerby for a few minutes, while at the same time defeating the tendency of people to "push all the buttons," or the equivalent, just to produce the most possible motion without paying attention to the lessons being offered. In the coupled-oscilliator display, this problem is addressed by making the different actions available in a certain sequence with a minimum required time interval between them.

We've found that some signs are necessary to direct the viewer's attention to certain aspects of the display and to provide simple explanations of the principles involved. The format adopted by the Exploratorium, "What to see and notice..., What is going on..." is usually appropriate. It is easy to arrange illumination on each sign when the corresponding demonstration is energized. Explanations should be brief and qualitative with a minimum of technical terms, and of course should be scrupulously correct. It is a good policy to have the explanatory text in mind while designing the demonstration. The texts used for our coupled-pendulum displays are given in the Appendix.

The Actuators

This set of animated displays uses six actuators. All are operated by identical gearhead motors, each consisting of a small shaded-pole induction motor geared down to 6 rpm or 10 s per revolution.[1] Consider the basic task of starting a simple pendulum, typically about 30 cm long. A hardwood "finger" about one-quarter the length of the pendulum, fitted with a metal hub, is attached to the motor output shaft. The finger is slightly grooved and its tip is rounded. Initially the finger is horizontal and positioned beneath the pendulum bob. As the motor turns, the finger comes up to the pendulum bob and pushes it aside until the bob slides off its tip (Fig. 2). Now the pendulum has started swinging while the finger continues down out of the way. The gearhead motor, after completing one revolution, must stop upon reaching its initial position, about one-quarter revolution before the finger contacts the pendulum bob again. Starting the pendulum takes about 3 s, and the remainder of the rotation goes largely unnoticed. To stop the motor at a predetermined point, a cam on its output shaft throws a microswitch. The cam is made from a pointer knob, bored through to accommodate the shaft. If the motor and the microswitch are connected to a circuit such as that in Fig. 3, the motor will run when line voltage is newly applied after being off, until the microswitch closes, then hold that position indefinitely. Each actuator assembly is mounted on a short 13-mm rod that can be clamped to an ordinary

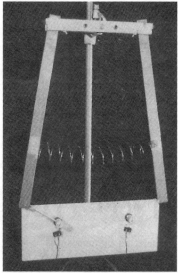

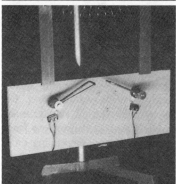

Fig. 4. (a–top) The coupled-pendulum pair about to be released in the antisymmetric mode. (b–bottom) Close-up of the counter-rotating dual actuators, at their resting positions. In this case the actuators are mounted on the same ring stand as the pendulum pair for stability of adjustment. Note the open "finger" used with the solid-bar pendulums.

Fig. 5. (a–top) Seven simple pendulums, three of them provided with actuators, suspended from a common bar. (b–bottom) Detail of the suspension of one end of the bar. The strings are about 0.1 m apart, 0.06 m long, and are clamped 0.02 m from the wall of the display case.

ring stand or similar support. Adaptations of this design are used to start different oscillators.

The Coupled-Pendulum Pair

This demonstration embodies the special case of two identical oscillators weakly coupled to each other. The coupled-pendulum pair itself was constructed locally a very long time ago. Each pendulum consists of a steel bar 6 by 25 mm, 0.45 m long, suspended near one end on a ball bearing so that the two can swing only

in their common plane. They are coupled by a light brass spring with force constant about 0.5 N/m, attached to each pendulum bar about two-thirds of its length from the pivot (Fig. 4). The set is provided with devices to facilitate starting the system manually in either of its normal modes. As is well known, in the symmetric normal mode the two pendulums remain parallel throughout the motion with the spring exerting no force, whereas in the antisymmetric normal mode the pendulums move

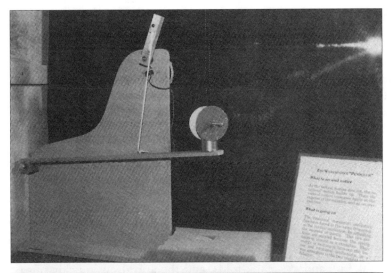

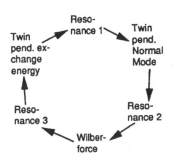

Fig. 7. Diagram showing the order of presentation. The viewer must touch a button to advance to the next demonstration. A minimum delay of 30 s is imposed at each step.

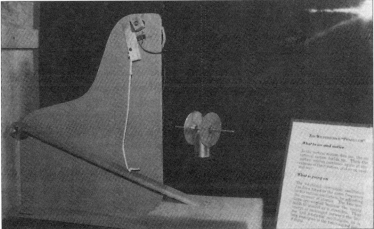

Fig. 6. (a–top) The folding-crank actuator, with the crank near its highest point just before releasing the Wilberforce oscillator. (b–bottom) A moment later the crank has folded, the arm has dropped away, and the oscillator is moving freely.

oppositely while the center of the spring remains stationary. Of particular interest also is the non-normal mode that results when one pendulum is started with the other at rest in its equilibrium position. In this mode, a full exchange of energy occurs periodically, with each pendulum in turn stopping momentarily at its equilibrium position.

For the animated display, two actuators turn in opposite senses and are located symmetrically beneath the two pendulums. When both are activated simultaneously, the coupled-pendulum pair is launched in the antisymmetric mode. If only one of the two actuators operates, the nonnormal mode just described results. (To keep the task of animation simple, the symmetric normal mode is not demonstrated; one can argue that it is easy to visualize, as compared with the other modes.)

The sense of rotation of one gearmotor was reversed by turning over the whole field magnet relative to the armature and frame. Instead of the wooden fingers described above, we used sturdier hairpin-shaped brass fingers on both actuators. These, being open in the center, avoid the possibility of the mechanism jamming if an already swinging rigid pendulum should run into a slowly rising solid finger. Their flatter form also makes it easier to synchronize the times of release of the pendulums.

Sympathetic Oscillation, or Resonance

The viewer, having observed the exchange of energy between the two identical pendulums, may then be presented with a more general case. As in the familiar classroom demonstration, several simple pendulums of assorted lengths are suspended from a common bar, which is itself free to swing, thereby coupling the pendulums. The fact to be conveyed is that when one pendulum is started, it will exchange a substantal fraction of its energy only with other pendulums of the same natural frequency, i.e., of equal length. There are three simple pendulums of 0.2-m length, two of 0.3 m, and two of 0.45 m. Each has, as its bob, a steel ball about 25 mm in diameter. The seven are equally spaced along a light horizontal wooden bar about 2 m long. The bar has a short crosspiece at each end, by which it is suspended from the walls of the display case with four strings 0.06 m long (Fig. 5). The length of the suspension of the bar must be significantly different from that of any of the pendulums so that its own resonant oscillation is not strongly excited. One pendulum of each of the three lengths is provided with one of the simple-pendulum actuators described above. When any one actuator operates, viewers can observe that both or all of the pendulums of one particular length are set swinging while the others achieve only small displacements.

The Wilberforce "Pendulum"

The history and analysis of this eye catching coupled-oscillator system, and references to earlier works, have been given by Whitaker[2] and by Berg and Marshall.[3] In our display, a commercial unit[4] is suspended from the ceiling of the display case. We wanted to launch the system by lifting the bob and dropping it quickly (as would be done by hand) and to adhere to the rule that the actuator should be clearly distinct from the system demonstrated. The lifter must be able to encounter the bob at any point in its motion and lift it slowly, then drop faster and farther than the bob itself when released.

A folding crank became our means to ac-complish this. A hardwood crank about 0.12 m long is attached to the usual gearmotor and cam. The crank is in two sections, joined at one side by a small hinge. From a peg near the end of the crank a nylon cord runs down to the center of a flat hardwood arm about 0.6 m long, supported at one end by a bearing. The free end of this arm is positioned beneath the Wiberforce pendulum bob (Fig. 6). When the motor turns, as long as there is torque on the crank in one sense, the crank remains straight and lifts the arm, which lifts the pendulum. When the crank passes the top of its motion, the torque on the crank reverses in sense, the crank folds, and the arm drops quickly out of the way of the Wilberforce pendulum. This seemingly Goldbergesque arrangement has worked flawlessly for several thousands of operations with no sign of trouble or undue wear.

Presentation

Each of the six oscillatory modes (three in the resonance demonstration, two in the identical pair, and the Wilberforce oscillation) persists for about a minute. It would be too much to expect the average viewer to wait until each motion has essentially died out before starting the next. If the motions follow one another too closely, however, a jumble of activity results that only serves to confuse. As a compromise, the six motions are made available in rotation in the order indicated in the diagram (Fig. 7). Each new motion occurs when the viewer touches a button, but the button is deactivated for about 30 s after the operation. Illuminated signs make it quite clear when the button is active and when it is not. Thus, the Wilberforce pendulum, which has longest decay time, can be operated only at intervals of at least three minutes. Similarly the three excitations of the resonance demonstration and the two modes of the coupled pair can be started only at times separated by at least one minute, so that each mode has time to decay sufficiently. Admittedly, it would be preferable to present the six actions in a more logical order, but the necessary delays would discourage casual viewers.

The circuit that orders and times the presentation is not described here in detail because

Appendix: The Signs Accompanying These Displays

Two Coupled Pendulums—I

What to see and notice

At any time, the amplitude of one pendulum is decreasing and the other is increasing. The process reverses only when one has fully stopped.

What is going on

The pendulum initially set into motion transmits a periodic force to the other, which opposes the motion of the first and aids that of the second. Once this relative phase has been established, the energy transfer continues in the same direction until all of the first pendulum's energy is exhausted. Only then does the phase reverse and the whole process repeats in the other direction. This is *not* one of the "normal modes" of the system.

Two Coupled Pendulums—II

What to see and notice

When the pendulums are started symmetrically,[5] each one continues to move with the same amplitude and a well-defined frequency.

What is going on

This system has two "normal modes." In this one, the spring's force has the same phase in relation to the motion of each pendulum. The system is, in effect, divided into two independent ones since the midpoint of the spring could as well be fixed in place.

In the other normal mode, not demonstrated here, the two pendulums swing parallel to each other, remaining the same distance apart, so the spring transmits no force.

Resonance

What to see and notice

When any one pendulum is set into motion, all of them move a little, but only other pendulums of the same length will reach a large amplitude.

What is going on

The pendulum that was started transmits a periodic force to all of the others, through the motion of the long bar above. If another pendulum has a different natural frequency, that force will sometimes aid and sometimes oppose its motion, so that no long-term change in its energy can occur. If its frequency is the same, the periodic force adds to its energy cumulatively on each swing, so the amplitude builds up, as in the two-pendulum display.

The Willberforce "Pendulum"

What to see and notice

As the vertical motion dies out, the rotational motion builds up. Then the vertical motion increases again at the expense of the rotation, and so on over and over.

What is going on

The rotational (torsional) oscillation has been tuned to the same frequency as the vertical oscillation, by adjusting the moment of inertia. The two motions are coupled because the spring tends to unwind as it stretches. Thus energy is exchanged between the linear and rotational oscillations, in a way analogous to the two coupled pendulums.

it utilizes obsolete components and archaic methods. In essence it is a scale-of-six counter operating relays that supply ac to the actuators and illuminated signs. Individual circuits like that in Fig. 3 make each motor stop after one turn, while its associated sign remains illuminated.

In its first incarnation, the coupled-oscillators display attracted enough attention that it remained in the display case for 30 weeks, during which time the button was pushed about 15,000 times. A few years later, after the display case had been relocated (because of departmental needs) to a less heavily traveled area, it gathered about 5000 button-pushes in 25 weeks. There were no mechanical breakdowns and no maintenance required in either period. Comments indicated that the display contributed to the education of graduate students, faculty members, and the dean of the college, as well as the undergraduates for whom it was intended.

References

1. H & R Co., 18 Canal St., P.O. Box 122, Bristol, PA 19007 often has odd lots of similar motors and other items useful in mechanizing displays.

2. R.J. Whitaker, *Phys. Teach.* **26**, 37 (1988).

3. R.E. Berg and T.S. Marshall, *Am. J. Phys.* **59**, 32 (1991).

4. From Central Scientific Co., a predecessor of that pictured in Ref. 3.

5. This is actually the antisymmetric mode. It was felt that this distinction might present an unnecessary complication for the average viewer.

Animated Displays V: Relaxation Oscillators

Paul Chagnon, Physics Department, University of Notre Dame,
Notre Dame, IN 46556

Around 1980, H.R. Crane presented a contributed paper at the AAPT summer meeting to promulgate the idea that in engineering-physics courses we should sometimes discuss simple systems involving more than one physics concept at a time. Crane mentioned several kinds of relaxation oscillators to illustrate the degree of complexity he felt appropriate. Eventually that talk became the basis for the exhibit described here; indeed, chronologically, this exhibit was the first in this "Animated Displays" series.

A good general definition of relaxation oscillators is not easy to come by. Perusal of several technical dictionaries turned up one or two mentions of the resistor-capacitor (RC) neon-lamp electrical oscillator only, and no other types. The ISPP group once enumerated some examples of relaxation oscillators and listed some of the common elements: a power source, some form of energy storage, and a trigger mechanism.[1] Crane later returned to the subject in his column in this journal,[2] this time emphasizing the synchronization of relaxation oscillators to external stimuli. In a footnote to that article, he characterized relaxation oscillators as not retaining their energy from cycle to cycle, in contrast to harmonic oscillators. A corollary is that, over some range of values, the frequency of a relaxation oscillator is roughly proportional to the power supplied to it.

To most people, "oscillator" implies free-running or astable oscillator. In that case the "trigger mechanism" consists of a nonlinear element resulting in a threshold characteristic, initiating some effect that reverses or undoes the buildup of energy that is characteristic of the cycle. There are also monostable oscillators analogous to the electrical univibrator, such as

Phys. Teach. **32**, 432 436 (Oct. 1994)

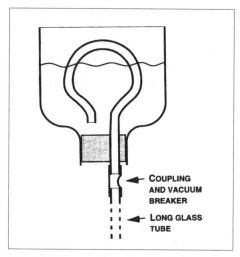

Fig. 1. Cross-section sketch of a Tantalus Cup. Water pours in continuously from above and is siphoned out intermittently.

the ordinary toilet flush,[3] and bistable ones, as the palm-glass oscillator described below.

In selecting examples for this exhibit, we deemed it desirable to let the oscillators provide all the action themselves. Of the examples often cited, only those that can be made to work with a period of a few seconds are eligible, ruling out most stick-and-slip phenomena. Others are ruled out for reasons of scale (geysers) or are too complex (biorhythms). We settled on two hydraulic examples, two thermal, and one electrical. A third hydraulic oscillator involving surface tension, namely droplet formation, is a good possibility not explored.

To supply water for the first pair mentioned, a recirculating system had to be set up in the display case. This is described in Appendix I. It proved to be less trouble than anticipated. The text of the signs accompanying this exhibit constitutes Appendix II.

The whole exhibit is controlled by a motion detector, as described previously,[4] except that the "drinking bird" runs continually to attract attention.

Tantalus' Cup

A siphon contained within an open vessel (Fig. 1) provides both the threshold effect and the means of "undoing" an accumulation of liquid in that vessel. Water supplied continuously but slowly from above rises steadily in the cup and equally in the left side of the siphon tube. When the water level reaches the top of the curved tube, before the cup is full, the siphon begins to flow and quickly empties the cup. Once the water level falls below the intake

of the siphon, air enters the tube, siphon action stops, and the cup begins to fill again.

Tantalus' Cup is described in Sutton's classic reference work[5] and surely goes back much further, since the siphon was known in ancient Greece. While the whole device is readily available from suppliers of laboratory and demonstration equipment, one can easily be improvised from the top of a bottle, as in Fig. 2. The rankest amateur glass-blower can fashion the siphon itself from glass tubing.

The weak point in the explanation given above lies in the interruption of the siphon when its intake is exposed to air. Actually a

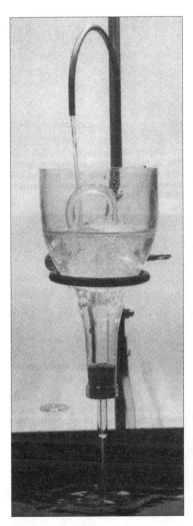

Fig. 2. Tantalus' Cup in operation. Normally the cup is set much higher, with an extension tube leading down, almost to the tray.

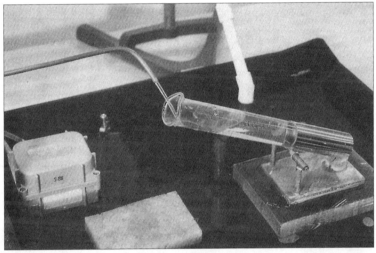

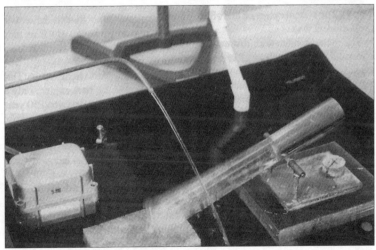

Fig. 3. Wild-boar scarer filling (top) and emptying (bottom). At the left is the recirculating pump, and the outlet of the chicken feeder is visible at the rear of the tray.

Fig. 4. Thermostat setup with spotlight, small fan, and relay all in operation.

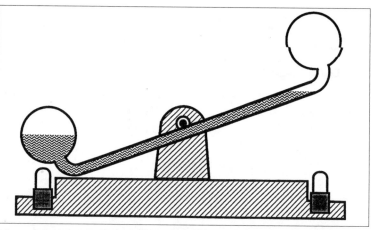

Fig. 5. Diagram of a palm-glass oscillator described in the text. Note that the pivot is placed low enough that the palm glass cannot balance stably.

siphon whose outlet is a few decimeters below the inlet, once started, will continue to pump an air-water mixture quite successfully over a sizable range of flow rates. An effective way to assure that the siphon stops every time is to provide a vacuum breaker (air inlet) just below the Tantalus Cup, where the siphon tube proper is coupled to a straight section of tubing leading farther down (Fig. 1). This is simply a hole cut in the side of the plastic connection that joins the tubes. If it is positioned properly, no water comes out, air goes in, and the reduced pressure difference weakens the siphon action sufficiently.

Wild-Boar Scarer

This device, usually formed from a length of bamboo and located in a gently falling stream, is to be found in some reproductions of Oriental gardens. The noise it makes is said to drive away wild animals; in one case boars[6] and in another merely deer.[7]

Ours consists of a 100-ml graduated cylinder, fitted into a brass tube that is pivoted on loose bearings fashioned of brass and copper tube fittings (Fig. 3). When the cylinder is empty, the heavier brass end rests on the base. Water rising in the cylinder eventually brings the center of gravity above the pivot, and the cylinder tips over. It quickly empties, the weighted end falls again, and the action repeats.

To reduce the jarring (there being very few wild boars to be scared away) and splashing, the open end falls on a sponge fixed in the water tray and the heavy end on a section of cork.

Thermostat

To simulate the action of a typical heating system, we connected an ordinary household thermostat, through a relay, to a lamp representing a furnace (Fig. 4). The system cycles on and off in a self-evident way.

The main problem with this exhibit is reduction of the cycle time to a few seconds. Setting the thermostat just a few degrees above the ambient temperature, removing the thermostat cover, and directing the 100-W spotlight on its works brings the heating time below 5 s. To achieve a comparable cooling time we direct a small fan, running continuously, at the thermostat.

Palm Glass and Drinking Bird.

Benjamin Franklin is said to be the originator of the palm glass or pulse glass. Two glass bulbs connected by a tube (Fig. 5) are filled with a volatile liquid, such as ethyl ether, and its vapor. When the lower bulb is warmed slightly, as in the palm of the hand, the increased vapor pressure drives liquid into the other bulb.

A palm glass[8] is easily converted into a heat engine or oscillator. A pivot, positioned below the mean center of gravity, results in a mechanically bistable configuration. A small light bulb

Interactive Physics Demonstrations

Fig. 6. Top, Palm-glass oscillator in motion. The right-hand bulb has just received enough liquid to overbalance the other, and is on the way down.

Fig. 7. Bottom, Drinking bird. The glass is for illustration only; actually this bird is motivated by a hot lamp under its tail.

Fig. 8. RC or neon-bulb oscillator. The right-hand meter calibrated 0-500 μC shows the charge accumulated, while the left-hand one reads the current or charging rate from 0-100 μC/s or μA. The power supply and a few other components are concealed behind the panel. A Plexiglas cover makes this demonstration safe to handle for classroom use.

at each end of the apparatus provides heat to whichever end is down, forcing liquid to the higher, cooler bulb on the other end until the palm glass flips to its complementary position. Thereupon the process reverses, and the cycle continues as long as the temperature differences are maintained. The example shown in Fig. 6 uses 12-V #1816 indicator lamps. Other models have 4-W, 120-V night-light bulbs, which are more convenient electrically but less compact.

For several years I believed that I had invented this little heat engine, only to find a variation of it described 50 years earlier by Sutton.[9] His intriguing version uses two sources of "cold," i.e., cool felt pads above the palm glass rather than heat sources below it. Later, I found that much earlier yet, "my" heat engine had appeared in *Scientific American* over a century ago.[10] Even better, that one is powered by sunlight falling on the lower bulb, the upper bulb being shaded by a raised screen. Direct solar power conversion at its simplest!

The asymmetric, monostable or single-ended form of the palm glass is the basis of the "drinking bird," fully explained elsewhere.[11] It is normally driven by the temperature difference resulting from evaporation of water at the bird's head. In our display (Fig. 7) a night-light supplies a little heat to the bird's other end. Even if the bird's drinking glass were kept full, the humidity due

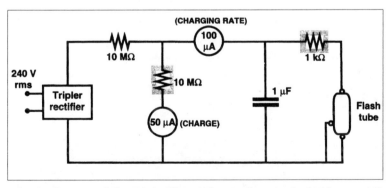

Fig. 9. Diagram of the RC oscillator. The power supply, fed by a small transformer, produces 1000 V at little current. Since the capacitance is 1μF, the voltmeter in effect reads charge in μC. Note that the Thévenin equivalent of the power supply, charging resistor, and voltmeter consists of a 500-V source in series with a 5-MΩ resistor. This works well with the 400-V threshold of the flashtube. The 1-KΩ resistor limits the discharge current in the flashtube to a reasonable value. It and the multiplier resistor for the voltmeter (both shaded) are concealed from view.

to other displays in the same display case would inhibit the necessary evaporation. Further, use of a heat source makes the display self-starting. In the normal configuration, if the bird misses one dip it is a dead duck.

Electrical RC Oscillator

Often called the neon-bulb oscillator, this best-known relaxation oscillator stands in close analogy to Tantalus' Cup, with a gaseous discharge serving as both the threshold effect and the means of quickly removing stored charge from the capacitor.

The RC circuit seen in Fig. 8 is scaled up and intended for classroom use, so it is fully enclosed in a box with a Plexiglas™ window. It uses a neon flashtube[12] (from an obsolete strobe lamp) that ignites at about 400 V. It would be worth experimenting with small xenon flashtubes from cameras or timing lights as alternatives.

Two meters indicate quantitatively both the accumulated charge and the charging rate or current (see Fig. 9 and its caption). The period of oscillation is about equal to the 5-s RC product, so the action is just slow enough that the meters, and in turn the viewer, can follow the cycles of charge and current.

Appendix I. Water System

As a precaution against splattering, a section of the display-case floor is lined with a 0.1-mm clear plastic sheet. On this rests a large photographic tray, about 0.4 by 0.5 m. Plastic trays of similar dimensions under the guise of "kiddie pools" may be found in toy stores. The displays that use flowing water are set up in this tray (see Figs. 2 and 3).

The heart of the system is an immersible pump[13] operating at reduced voltage. This pump sits in a corner of the tray and recirculates the distilled water to the displays through plastic hoses and 3-mm copper tubes. Tubing clamps of the screw-compressor type, on the plastic hoses, provide fine adjustment of the flow rates.

The system loses a few litres of water per week through evaporation and spattering. To extend the time between replenishments and to maintain a more constant water level in the tray, we include a "chicken feeder" that holds about 10 ℓ of additional water. While this is itself a relaxation oscillator, its action is too long-term to merit calling to the viewer's attention.

To enhance the visibility of the water against the dark background of the tray, we add a bit of fluorescein dye to the water, rendered slightly alkaline, and illuminate the whole tray with concealed ultraviolet lamps. This imparts a green glow to the water. Of course ordinary food coloring could be used instead.

Appendix II. Text of Signs for the Displays

Relaxation Oscillators

These illustrate several principles of physics. What properties are common to all these examples? A great many repetitive processes in real life are timed by relaxation oscillations, not harmonic oscillations. Some examples are your heartbeat, your respiration, geysers, blinkers, the cycling of furnaces and air conditioners, etc. How many more can you think of?

Tantalus' Cup

When the water *inside* the siphon tube reaches its top, the siphon starts and drains the whole vessel. Letting in air "breaks" the siphon, allowing the cup to fill again.

(In mythology, Tantalus, king of Lydia, did something unmentionable and was condemned to an unquenchable thirst.)

In the realm of plumbing, this is the heart of the "auto-flush" device found in some public restrooms.

Wild-Boar Deterrent

The oscillator just to the right has its origin in the Far East. Make one of bamboo and place it in a water stream in your garden. The noise it makes is said to scare away wild boars. (No wild boars have been reported in the display case since it has been in operation.)

Thermostat

The thermostat proper is an electrical switch operated by thermal expansion and contraction. This one has its cover removed. When the house cools off, the switch closes and turns on the furnace (represented by the lamp). When the temperature rises to a set value, the switch opens and turns off the furnace.

Thermal Oscillator

The lower bulb is heated; the increased vapor pressure forces liquid into the upper bulb, and the glass is overbalanced. The process then repeats, with the roles of the two bulbs interchanged. This is an adaptation of Benjamin Franklin's "palm glass."

Dippy Duck

The Drinking Bird craze swept the country in the 1950s. This is a variation of the thermal palm-glass oscillator displayed nearby. When the bird tips forward, its beak is supposed to soak up a little water from the glass. The bird's fuzzy head is thus kept moist, and evaporative cooling provides the temperature difference to keep the oscillation going. We are supplying heat to the bird's other end, as a substitute.

Electrical Relaxation Oscillator (RC Circuit)

As charge accumulates in the capacitor, its potential difference increases. When a certain value is reached, the gas-filled flash tube conducts, giving a pulse of light and partially discharging the capacitor. The capacitor recharges more quickly when its potential difference is low, and the rate tapers off as the charge increases.

The right-hand meter shows the amount of charge in the capacitor. The left-hand one shows the rate at which charge is supplied to the capacitor.

[Individual components are labeled inside the box, and the function of each is mentioned.]

References

1. Earl Zwicker, *ISPP Reminder*, September 1987 (unpublished). ISPP is a famous Chicago-area physics alliance whose name is derived from a predecessor, the Illinois State Physics Project; see *Phys. Teach.* 17, 576 (1979).

2. H.R. Crane, *Phys. Teach.* 27, 470 (1989).

3. Crane, loc. cit.

4. P.R. Chagnon, "Animated Displays II: Multiple Reflections," *Phys. Teach.* 30, 488 (1992).

5. R.M. Sutton, *Demonstration Experiments in Physics* (McGraw-Hill New York, 1938), sec. M-278, p. 110.

6. Butchart Gardens, Vancouver Island, British Columbia.

7. Japanese Garden, Portland, Oregon.

8. For example, #77730 from Central Scientific Co. (800-26-CENCO); under U.S. $20.

9. Sutton, op. cit, sec. H-73, p. 216.

10. "Thermoscopic Balance," *Sci. Am.* LVI, 134 (1887); reprinted in G.M. Hopkins, *Experimental Science* (Munn & Co., New York, 1889), p. 185.

11. K.B. Kolb, *Phys. Teach.* 4, 121 (1966); R. Mentzer, *Phys. Teach.* 31, 126 (1993); Crane, loc. cit.

12. General Radio type 631-P1; made by Sylvania.

13. Model P-AAA, Little Giant Pump Co., Oklahoma City, OK 73112.

Echo Tube

Joe Pizzo, Department of Physics, Lamar University,
Beaumont, TX 77710

The phenomenon of dispersion (frequency dependence of wave speed) is the basis for some spectacular demonstrations. The most outstanding example in optics is the separation of white light into the visible spectrum. Is there a similar demonstration for sound waves? Can "white" noise be separated into its audible spectrum? Since all frequencies of sound travel at the same speed in air, the answer to these questions would seem to be no. Nevertheless, if a pulse of sound waves (hand clap or finger snap) is created near the open end of a tube that is long compared to its diameter, the "echoes" or returning reflected waves seem to exhibit some type of dispersive behavior. The result is a sharp reflection of the original pulse, followed by a loud, ricochet-like "Zing" that begins on a high pitch and descends rapidly to a low pitch. In other words, an audible spectrum is played out in time by

the echo tube just as the visible spectrum is laid out in space by a prism.

This dispersive behavior in an "echo tube" is not the result of wave-speed variation with frequency. It is due to the difference in travel time for different frequencies of sound waves which have been reflected off the wall of the tube. Because of interference, only a particular frequency can be propagated down the tube at a particular "grazing angle" (angle between a ray and the axis of the tube). As a result, higher frequencies are reinforced for smaller grazing angles, make fewer reflections, and take less time to travel down the tube and back than the lower frequencies, which are reinforced at a larger grazing angle and make more reflections before returning. A detailed analysis of this phenomenon has been presented by Frank Crawford in an article entitled "Culvert Whistlers."[1] This article should be required

Fig. 1. An "echo tube" made from two sections of 18 in diam Sonotube, joined by a Sonotube collar of slightly larger diameter.

Phys. Teach. **24**, 428-429 (Oct. 1986)

reading for anyone who intends to set up an echo tube as a physics exhibit, since the explanation is much more complex than the construction.

The actual construction of an echo tube is the essence of simplicity, once the material is obtained. The main ingredient is the tube itself, which is made of sections of cardboard forms uscd to cast cement columns. The trade name for these forms, which can be purchased from building specialty suppliers, is "Sonotube." The forms are available in 20-foot sections with diameters ranging from 12 in to 36 in. An echo tube can be assembled from any number of these sections. At the Exploratorium, the echo tube is composed of five sections of 18-in diam Sonotube and extends an impressive 100 feet, beginning at ear level and sloping up to the roof.[2]

The echo tube described in this article is a modest version, consisting of two 20-foot sections with an 18-in diam (see Fig. 1). A collar to join the sections was made from a one-foot length of 20-in diam Sonotube which was spilt, reduced, and taped snugly around the joint of the two sections. The collar could be glued or bolted, but a friction fit was preferred in this setting so the tube could easily be moved to another location when desired.

This whole demonstration can be placed at the ear level of the intended audience in a variety of ways, or, if the exhibit is intended for children, it could rest on the floor allowing the participants to sit in front of it and delight themselves with the echoes and dispersions of their sounds.

References

1. Frank S. Crawford, *Am. J. Phys.* **39**, 610 (1971).

2. R. Hipschman, *Exploratorium Cookbook II*, (The Exploratorium, San Francisco, 1980), pp. 114.1–114.3.

Ambient Noise Resonators (There's Music in the Air)

Joe Pizzo, Department of Physics, Lamar University, Beaumont, TX 77710

Fig. 1. As Vanessa moves her ear from pipe to pipe, she hears the notes of the scale reinforced according to the length of the pipes.

From all the noise in the hallway, an open pipe will selectively reinforce that part of the sound with a wavelength equal to twice the length of the pipe. It follows from this fact that eight pieces of pipe can be cut to reproduce a musical scale. When these eight pieces are placed together in the hallway, participants can delight themselves with musical selections "picked out of the air" as they move their ear from one pipe to another (Fig. 1).

This system of ambient noise resonators is one of the least expensive hallway exhibits that can be constructed. The pipes are cut from the cardboard tubes that support carpet rolls. They usually come in 12-foot sections and can be obtained free from most carpet companies.

Phys. Teach. **24**, 312-313 (May 1986)

The length to which each tube is cut depends on the frequency, f, of the desired note.

$$L = V/(2f) \qquad (1)$$

where the speed of sound, V, depends on the average Celsius temperature, t, according to the approximation

$$V = 331 + 0.6t \text{ m/s}. \qquad (2)$$

The tubes in our exhibit are cut for the tempered scale, beginning one octave below middle C, (see Table I).

Figure 2 shows the final assembly of the tubes which are fastened to each other with ordinary nuts and bolts. A stand is provided to bring the exhibit to the ear level of the intended audience.

It should be noted that the radius of the tube will make a slight difference in the resonant frequency due to an "edge effect" at each end. It is possible to compensate for this effect by using, instead of Eq. (1), the equation

$$L = V/(2f) - 1.22r \qquad (3)$$

where r is the radius of the tube. The tubes in our exhibit are cut according to Eq. (1) and give a surprisingly faithful rendition of the scale.

Table I. This table shows the frequencies of the notes in the tempered scale for the octave below "Middle C," along with the length of open pipe which will "pick these notes out of the air."

Note	Frequency (Hz)	Length (m)
C	130.81	1.32
D	146.83	1.17
E	164.81	1.04
F	174.61	0.99
G	196.00	0.88
A	220.00	0.78
B	246.94	0.70
C	261.63	0.66

Fig. 2. The tubes are assembled according to length and fastened to each other with nuts and bolts.

Interference and Diffraction Corridor Demonstrations

G.R. Davies, Physics Department, University of Natal, Private Bag X01, Scottsville, 3209 Pietermaritzburg, South Africa

A previous article[1] reported on a set of "hands-on" corridor demonstrations that make up our mini-exhibition on polarized light. We now wish to describe a corresponding set that illustrates various aspects of interference and diffraction — not only for light waves but other types too. Most readers will be familiar with at least some of the items, but those planning some similar display may find it helpful to have several demonstrations described in one piece.

Although our exhibits are intended primarily for our physics students, the signs accompanying the demonstrations are worded in such a way that the general passerby can also take part. As before, the emphasis is on "hands-on" rather than "don't touch."

Quincke Tube

A simple form of Quincke tube, constructed mainly from copper pipe and plumbers' fittings (elbows, tees, and reducers) and incorporating a trombone-type slide, demonstrates interference of sound waves (Fig. 1). For a given frequency (e.g., 3.0 kHz) and with the ear close to the outlet cone, a maximum sound is heard when the two path lengths are the same. As the sliding portion is pushed out, minima and maxima are observed. The distance moved from one minimum to the next can be read from a scale, and hence the wavelength de-

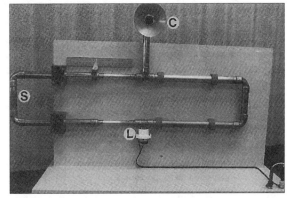

Fig. 1. Quincke tube: (L) loudspeaker, (S) sliding tube, (C) outlet cone.

duced. This in turn permits an estimate of the speed of sound in air to be made, since the frequency is known.

Double-Slit Interference Fringes—Air and Water[2]

A laser beam (broadened by a lens) is bisected by the surface of water in a fish tank (Fig. 2). A double-slit slide is fixed to the near end of the tank in the path of the beam and a ground glass screen located at the other end. The interference patterns formed by the laser light in passing through air and water appear on the screen, one above the other, and the fringe spacings are compared. Four water fringe spacings are seen to occur below three air fringe spacings, corresponding to the ratio of the wavelength in air to that in water.

Lloyd's Mirror — Microwave Version

A scaled-up version of the Lloyd's mirror interference arrangement can be per-

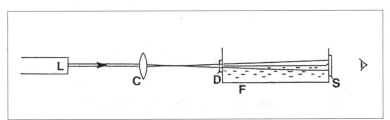

Fig. 2.   Double-slit interference — air and water: (L) laser, (C) converging lens, (D) double-slit slide, (F) fish tank, (S) ground-glass screen.

Phys. Teach. **33**, 244-247 (April 1995)

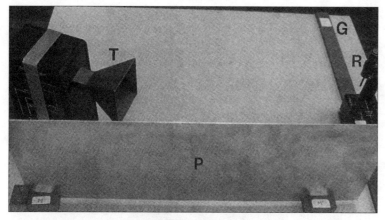

Fig. 3. Lloyd's mirror — microwave version: (T) transmitter, (P) metal plate, (R) receiver, (G) guide for receiver.

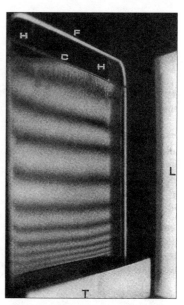

Fig. 4. Thin-film interference: (F) metal frame, (T) narrow tank containing weak detergent solution, (C) crossbar, (H) hooks with threads attached, (L) lamp box with translucent screen.

formed using microwaves (Fig. 3). As the detector is moved along a guide perpendicular to the "mirror" (a metal plate), maxima and minima are observed. In particular, a *minimum* is noted when the detector is close to the plate (due to the phase change on reflection); the response increases when the plate is removed.

Thin-Film Interference

A smooth metal rod that has been bent into an inverted broad U-shape (25 by 25 cm) stands in front of a matte black screen, with its "feet" in a narrow tank containing a 1% to 2% solution of a good quality detergent. A stiff wire crossbar whose ends loop around the vertical sides of the bent rod can be pulled upwards by means of a pair of threads, thereby drawing up a very thin film (Fig. 4). The film is illuminated by white light from a translucent screen at the front of a nearby lamp box. Horizontal multicolored bands are observed, which drift slowly downwards as the film drains down. It is also interesting to view these bands through a color filter. The lifetime of the film is of course dependent on ambient conditions. The film strength can be improved by the addition of glycerine, but the interference pattern is then likely to be less regular.

Newton's Rings in White Light

Newton's rings may be easily observed without a microscope if they are formed using two lens surfaces (one convex, the other concave) of

only slightly different radii of curvature. When set up using a white light source, the effect of interposing red and green filters can be observed — the red set of rings is larger than the green set because of the increased wavelength.

Wedge-Film Interference — Air and Water

Mention has been made elsewhere[3] of a method of determining the refractive index of water relative to air by wedge-film interference. If a bubble of air is deliberately trapped in a wedge-shaped water film (formed between slightly inclined glass blocks) and illuminated by monochromatic light, the fringe spacings can be compared. Four water fringe spacings are seen to lie opposite three air fringe spacings, corresponding to the refractive index of water relative to air. (A sealant can be applied all around the edge of the block assembly to provide a more permanent unit.)

Single-Slit Diffraction

A laser beam can be directed through an adjustable slit and the effect of altering the slit width noted.

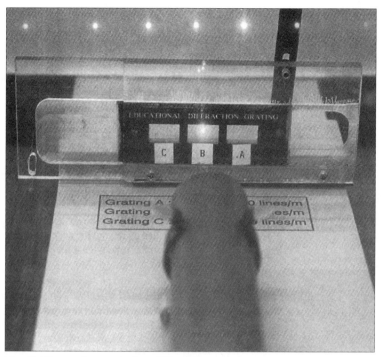

Fig. 5. Above, transmission diffraction gratings arrangement.

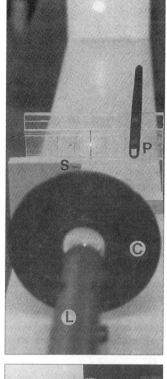

Transmission-Type Diffraction Grating

In this exhibit, a lever enables any one of three diffraction gratings mounted on a card[4] to be placed in the path of a laser beam (Fig. 5). The gratings have different numbers of lines per unit length; the greatest number of diffracted beams is seen to occur when using the grating having the fewest lines per unit length.

Diffraction by Various Obstacles

A straight edge, a ball bearing, and a wire can be successively placed in the path of a laser beam that has been broadened by a lens (Fig. 6) and the corresponding diffraction (and interference) effects observed.

Diffraction by Circular Holes

Four small discs, each having a hole of a different diameter (40 to 200 μm),[5] are mounted on a large vertical disc. The small discs are all accurately located at the same radius and at 90° positions (Fig. 7). As the large disc is turned in its own plane, "click-stops" enable any selected hole to be placed in the path of a laser beam and the corresponding diffraction pattern observed on a screen.

Fig. 6. Top, at right, diffraction by various obstacles: (P) Perspex (Plexiglas) slide carrying a wire and a ball bearing, (S) straight edge, (C) converging lens, (L) laser.

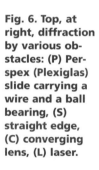

Fig. 7. Arrangement for diffraction by circular holes.

The screen should preferably be provided with a hood to reduce background light. Initial alignment of the laser beam is critical, so the supporting stand needs to be provided with a levelling/clamping facility.

Diffraction by a Set of Small Obstacles

A small round obstacle produces diffraction rings similar to those of a small round hole of the same diameter. The intensity of the pattern is enhanced if a number of such obstacles placed close together are used.

In this well-known demonstration, the "obstacles" are human red blood cells in a very thin dried smear on a microscope slide. (There is an art in obtaining a good smear; the advice of the nearest medical technologist may be useful here.) The slide is placed in the path of a laser beam and the corresponding pattern displayed on a screen 0.20 m further on. A scale on the screen enables the radius, r, of the first dark ring to be measured. Then, assuming the wavelength, λ, of the laser light is known, the diameter, d, of the blood cells can be estimated since, for a small angle of diffraction θ,

$$\sin\theta \cong \theta = \frac{1{,}22\lambda}{d} \qquad (1)$$

and

$$\theta \cong \frac{r}{0{,}20} \qquad (2)$$

so

$$d \cong \frac{0{,}24\lambda}{r} \qquad (3)$$

Reflection Type of Diffraction Grating

A long-play record can be used as a simple reflection grating[6] and has the advantage over a compact disc in that, due to the larger "spacing," several orders can readily be displayed on a screen alongside one another.

A slide projector is used to focus an image of a slit on a screen. The long-play record, mounted vertically, is pushed by the operator along guides (against the action of a spring) so that a limited portion of one of its faces intercepts the projector beam at a glancing angle of 5 to 10 degrees. Several colored spectra are then observed on the screen, as well as the zero-order white light beam. The operator is asked

to note which color is diffracted the most in any spectrum (relative to the zero-order beam) and to consider whether this is the same as for a transmission type of diffraction grating. Afterwards, the spring returns the record to its position out of the beam.

Other possible additions to a collection could include diffraction by a rotatable mesh, and interference between light reflected from the inner and outer surfaces of a glass tube.[7] For further ideas (as well as alternative versions of some of the demonstrations described here), consult Refs. 8 through 11.

A final caution: In view of the "open" nature of these displays, departments are advised to secure the lasers and other expensive items suitably, to reduce the risk of theft.

References

1. G.R. Davies, *Phys. Teach*, **28**, 464 (1990).
2. A.T. Mogill, *Phys. Teach*, **13**, 555(1975).
3. G.R. Davies, *Am. J. Phys.* **44**, 1215. (1976).
4. A set of three diffraction gratings on a card is manufactured by Paton Hawksley Electronics Ltd., Rockhill Labs, Keynsham, Bristol, England.
5. Pinhole sets are obtainable, for example, from Edmund Scientific, 101 E Gloucester Pike, Barrington, NJ 08007-1380.
6. G.R. Davies, *Sch. Sci. Rev.* (UK) **76**, 81 (1994).
7. W.C. Maddox et al., *Am. J. Phys.* **44**, 387 (1976).
8. R. Sutton, *Demonstrating Experiments in Physics* (McGraw-Hill, New York, 1938).
9. *Physics Demonstration Experiments*, edited by H. Meiners (Ronald Press, New York, 1970).
10. G.D. Freier and F.J. Anderson, *Demonstration Handbook for Physics* (AAPT, College Park, MD, 1981).
11. C. Siddons, *Experiments in Physics* (Basil Blackwell, Oxford, 1988).

A Wave Machine

Joe Pizzo, Department of Physics, Lamar
University, Beaumont, TX 77710

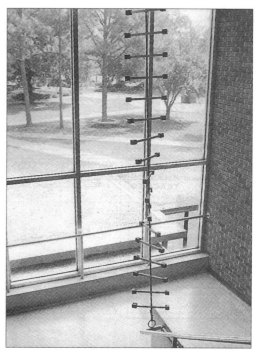

Fig. 1. A device for observing transverse waves at low speed has been set up in the stairwell of the Physics building at Lamar University.

A high stairwell provides the opportunity to demonstrate transverse waves in relatively slow motion, using an exhibit like the one shown in Fig. 1. To construct such a "wave machine," the following items will be required: Rubber tubing, a smooth metal ring, clamps, machine screws and hex nuts, wood strips, and wood cubes.

The wood strips (shown in Fig. 2) are approximately 5 mm thick and almost 2 cm wide, having been cut from the side of a "1 by 4." The length of the strips is a factor in the rotational inertia of the device and should be chosen accordingly. In our device, the strips are 30 cm long. The wood cubes are approximately 3.5 cm on a side with a 1-cm deep notch in one face. The notch is just wide enough to accept the ends of two strips wedged together (see Fig. 2). The wood cubes were cut from pieces of a "2 by 4" that had been split lengthwise. For the purpose of reference, a set of two strips, wedged and glued into a cube at each end, will be called a "spoke."

The spokes should be assembled with the rubber tubing passing through as shown in Fig. 2. The hex nuts should not be tightened securely until the exhibit is mounted with tension in the tubing and all spokes are aligned in the same plane.

The tubing at the bottom of the assembly can be clamped around a smooth metal ring, which in turn can be attached to a railing with a hose clamp (see Fig. 1). This method has been found to facilitate the initiation of a wave. While tension is applied to the tubing at the top of the assembly, attachment can be made to the ceiling in an appropriate manner.

When a lower spoke is given a twist, the torsional motion is transmitted up the rubber tubing. The speed of the wave can be controlled by the tension in the tubing and/or the rotational inertia of the spokes. The wave speed

Fig. 2. Rubber tubing is passed through the assembled spokes. The machine screws and hex nuts (on each side of the tubing) provide a means of tightening the spokes of the tubing.

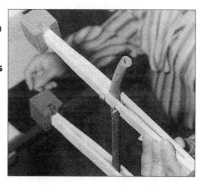

in our exhibit is low enough (50 cm/s) that a pulse can be studied easily. A travelling wave can be generated by a repetitive twisting motion on the lowest spoke. Moreover, since reflections occur at the ceiling, a standing wave can be set up with some practice.

The idea for this exhibit came from an article by Clayton, Downing, and Callaway,[1] describing a classroom demonstration constructed from soda straws and sewing elastic.

Reference

1. Glen T. Clayton, Harry D. Downing, and Thomas O. Callaway, *Am. J. Phys.* **49,** 375 (1981).

Phys. Teach. **24,** 173 (March 1986)

A Longitudinal Wave Machine

Joe Pizzo, Department of Physics, Lamar University, Beaumont, TX 77710

Once you have made the decision to place interactive physics demonstrations in your hallways and corridors, you should think about installing exhibits that relate to one another. One of the most satisfying learning experiences to be derived from the use of interactive demonstrations is the discovery of connections between related exhibits.

A case in point is the transverse wave machine described previously in this column.[1] The existence of a device that allows participants to create and watch transverse waves called out for a companion that would exhibit longitudi-

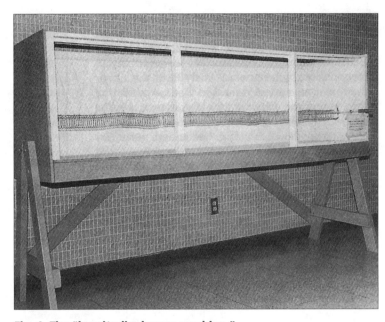

Fig. 1. The "longitudinal wave machine."

nal waves. Several commercial devices are available (see, for example, the *PASCO Scientific 1988 Catalog,* p. 66), but most of these are too expensive to be left unattended in the hallway.

R. Dean Ayers at California State University, Long Beach, has constructed a longitudinal wave machine from a long Slinky, some string, and paper clips, that is quite durable and sustains longitudinal waves with very little damping and relatively slow speed. This paper describes a slightly more substantial version that was copied from Professor Ayers. Figure 1 shows the longitudinal wave machine constructed from a long Slinky coil which was obtained from Frey Scientific Company.[2] The length of the stretched section in our device is 225 cm and contains 180 coils. This gives an average spacing of slightly more than 1 cm per coil, which seems to be optimum. (If the spacings are much larger the pulses become less dis-

tinct and travel too fast. Smaller spacing allows well-defined pulses that travel slowly, but the overall length is too short.) The Slinky is supported by two 40-cm strands of fishing line (in the form of a "v") attached by snap swivels at every eighth coil. The upper ends of the support strands are attached to pieces of quarter-round molding running along the upper length of the apparatus. The two lengths of molding are separated by 50 cm and nailed to the frame of the device. The frame shown in Fig. 1 is much more complicated than it has to be and, in retrospect, it seems that a simple plywood base would have worked better.

The biggest trick is alignment of the Slinky, both vertically and horizontally. We first tried to align the coils as they were strung but soon found that to be a frustrating, if not impossible task. Our solution was to set up ring stands at each end of the device to support a 225-cm length of PVC pipe which had a diameter

Phys. Teach. **27,** 54-55 (Jan. 1989)

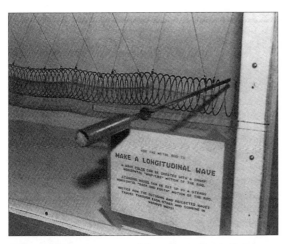

Fig. 2. The wave machine is activated by an aluminum bar attached to a supported coil at one end of the apparatus. The narrow slit in the Plexiglas window restricts motion to a single horizontal direction along the length of the Slinky.

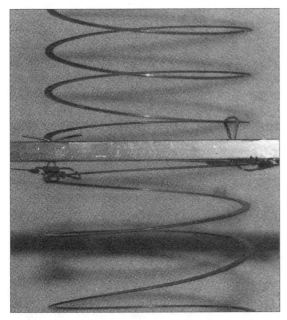

Fig. 3. The aluminum bar is connected to the coil with cotter pins.

slightly smaller than the Slinky's. After the PVC pipe was leveled and aligned horizontally, the Slinky was slipped onto the pipe, stretched over its length, and damped at each end. This held the Slinky coils "in place" while the support strings were attached. When the stringing was finished, the pipe and ring stands were removed and the ends of the Slinky were at-

tached to plywood boards installed at each end of the apparatus. Since the horizontal tension was uniform over the length of the stretched Slinky, the coils remained in place.

One possible method for using the exhibit is simply to grasp the coils at one end and set up longitudinal waves by hand. However, when that option was offered, many participants ignored the word "horizontal" in the graphics and pumped the Slinky up and down. Such interaction not only leaves an incorrect impression of a longitudinal wave, it can also create a tangled mess of coils and strings. Our solution to this problem is shown in Fig. 2. A Plexiglas cover denies direct access to the coils by hand, while a narrow (1 cm wide) slit in the Plexiglas allows only horizontal motion of the coils by an aluminum bar. This bar is attached to the coils by cotter pins as shown in Fig. 3. It is important to attach the bar to coils that are directly supported or else the torque on the bar will pull that part of the Slinky out of vertical alignment.

The graphics shown in Fig. 2 read as follows:

Use the Metal Rod to Make a Longitudinal Wave

A wave *pulse* can be created with a sharp horizontal "whip-like motion" of the rod.
Standing waves can be set up by a steady horizontal "back and forth motion" of the rod.

(Notice how the outgoing and reflected waves travel through each other and combine in various ways.)

At another place near the exhibit, the observers are asked to check out the transverse wave machine in the stairwell of our building and note similarities and differences.

References

1. Joe Pizzo, "A Wave Machine," *Phys. Teach.* **24**, 173 (1986).

2. Catalog #2642, Frey Scientific Company, 905 Hickory Lane, Mansfield, OH 44905 (Phone: 800-225-FREY).

Chapter 4

Optics

Deck the Halls ...
with interactive corridor demonstrations

Joe Pizzo, Department of Physics, Lamar University,
Beaumont, TX 77710

One of the most effective ways of presenting Sciences to the nonscientist is through the use of interactive exhibits. Rob Semper of the Exploratorium defines an interactive exhibit as one in which "some of the characteristics of the actual phenomenon are made accessible to manipulation or alteration by the user."[1] The Exploratorium, a science museum founded by Frank Oppenheimer in San Francisco, has been a pioneer in the development of such exhibits.[2] Many other museums have since followed the lead and have taken displays from behind glass cases, allowing the public direct access to the phenomena.

In order to encourage such endeavors, *The Physics Teacher* will feature a one-page, monthly column on interactive hallway exhibits. We welcome the submission of manuscripts detailing the construction of such exhibits which have been tested in a hallway-type setting, where security is at a minimum and supervision is unnecessary.

We will not ordinarily be interested in displays that are one dimensional and static. Active participation should be a necessary ingredient of the exhibit. The description should emphasize construction and presentation, as opposed to theoretical exposition. Photographs or sketches showing the details of the exhibit would be helpful.

In general, we have several words of advice for anyone wishing to set up a series of hallway exhibits.

- **Keep the graphics to a minimum.** Interactive means doing, as opposed to reading. Participants should feel free to experiment and discover on their own. On the other hand, there must be some means of suggesting that a passerby should interact with the exhibit. We have found that this can be

Phys. Teach. **24**, 101 (Feb. 1986)

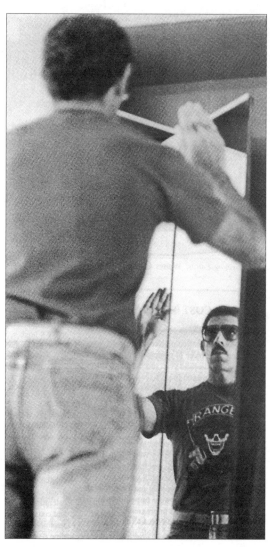

Fig. 1. When the participant raises his right hand, the image in the right-angle mirror also raises its right hand.

done by the design of the exhibit itself, a brief invitation, or a photograph of someone using the exhibit.

- **Construction must be sturdy** — these exhibits are designed to be used. Secure all expensive parts. Consider all possible hazards and either eliminate them or shield them from participants.

- **Someone should be assigned** the task of making a daily inspection of the exhibits and performing routine maintenance as necessary. A broken exhibit should never be left out on display.

- **Try to include** (and call attention to) exhibits that relate to each other.

To get you started, we will describe a very simple (but highly popular) exhibit:

See Yourself as Others See You

We have constructed a special mirror, using two "full-length" mirrors from a discount department store. The mirrors are mounted on two pieces of 3/4-in plywood that have been attached to each other at a right angle and held firmly in place with right-angle brackets. The mirrors are butted right up against each other.

The whole right-angle mirror assembly is positioned in the hallway in such a way that a passerby must look toward the vertex, as shown in Fig. 1. When a participant raises his right hand, as invited, the results are amazing. Most people gasp audibly when their image also raises its right hand. An invitation to determine how the light rays travel is taken seriously. Consequently, the mirrors must be cleaned at least once a week.

References

1. R. Sander, J. Diamond, M. St. John, *Am. J. Phys.* **50**, 425 (1982).

2. The Exploratorium publishes "recipes" which outline the construction details of their exhibits. For information on their "Cookbooks," as well as other publications, write to: The Exploratorium Store, 3601 Lyon St., San Francisco, CA 94123.

The Nonreversing Mirror with a Twist

T.H. Ansbacher, Museum of Science and Industry, 57th Street and Lakeshore Drive, Chicago, IL 60637

I f a plane mirror reverses left and right, why doesn't it reverse up and down? If two plane mirrors at right angles do *not* reverse left and right, why *do* they reverse up and down when the arrangement is turned sideways? A display including a right-angle mirror that may be rotated makes an eye-catching demonstration that allows observers to answer those questions for themselves.

The construction of the display is simple and inexpensive, as shown in Fig. 1. The right-angle mirrors are mounted on a frame built of 12-mm (1/2-in) plywood, and ordinary rear-surfaced mirrors can be used without causing an objectionably visible joint. The pivot, which allows the arrangement to be turned sideways, uses a 12-mm-diam (1/2-in) steel rod and standard laboratory mounting flanges. One flange is attached to the mirror frame with a set screw

holding the rod in place. The other flange is attached to a wall or suitable frame and serves as a bearing.

It would be good pedagogy to display a single plane mirror next to the rotary right-angle mirror, in which case the single mirror and the apex of the right-angle mirror should be in the same plane so that both produce images an equal distance from the viewer. Also, so that both images can be seen at the same time, the mirror arrangements should be angled slightly toward each other.

The question of left-right reversal by a mirror is an excellent one for discussion, because the phenomena are directly accessible to students and present puzzling aspects that require careful thought and definition of terms for their clarification.[1] To clear up the "question," it becomes necessary to distinguish between

Phys. Teach. **25**, 104-105 (Feb. 1987)

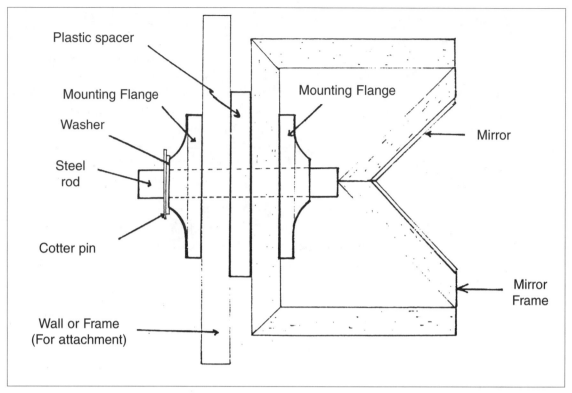

Plastic spacer

Mounting Flange

Washer

Steel rod

Cotter pin

Wall or Frame
(For attachment)

Mounting Flange

Mirror

Mirror
Frame

Fig. 1. A (cut-away) side view detailing the pivot and mounting for a right-angle mirror that can be rotated.

two different meanings of the terms "left" and "right." In one meaning, these designate the two halves of the bilaterally symmetric body or directions with respect to the body. In the other meaning, the terms designate the kind of symmetry possessed by hands, corkscrews, etc. (more properly designated left-handed and right-handed symmetry). To understand how a mirror changes right-handed objects into left-handed images — that is, does optically what cannot be done physically — it becomes necessary to understand just how a mirror image is formed in the first place.

Some questions can be posted along with the demonstration to stimulate thought along these lines. For example:

• Does a mirror really reverse left and right? What does this mean?

• What is the evidence for the left-right reversal?

• If a mirror reverses left and right, does it also reverse east and west?

• If the double-mirror combination does not reverse left and right, why does it reverse up and down when turned sideways?

References

1. Mirror images and left-right symmetry are touched on by most introductory physics textbooks. For a more complete discussion, see Martin Gardner, *The Ambidextrous Universe* (Basic Books, NY, 1964). For a different approach to the subject, see Kenneth W. Ford, *Phys. Teach.* **13**, 228 (1975).

Hands-On Optics Demonstration Unit

Byron E. Leonard, Department of Mathematics-Physics, The School of the Ozarks, Point Lookout, MO 65726

The optics display and demonstration unit described here is the culmination of ideas conceived over a period of time. The basic intent was to utilize two large lenses, one concave and one convex, several prisms, mirrors, and other optical items in a system that would be useful not only as an educational instrument but be entertaining as well. Even though there are many configurations for the optics, some of which were tested, the final design is near optimum for its intended use.

Description of Unit

Fig. 1 shows the components of the unit. Two commercial multiple-ray projectors provide the narrow (~3 mm) light beams. These have the capability of varying the angle of all but the center beam. The two ray projectors

Fig. 1. Overall view of demonstration unit. Component identification numbers: 1) multiple-ray projector; 2) "finger holes" in acrylic cover, 6.5 cm diam; 3) switch; 4) diffraction grating; 5) plano-concave lens; 6) plano-convex lens; 7) beam splitter; 8) diffraction grating patterns; 9) twisted prisms; 10) curved mirrors; 11) rotatable multiple mirror unit; 12) equiangular prism; 13) transmission-reflection filter; 14) plane mirrors; 15) matte-white projection screen material; and 16) decorative "logo." Overall dimensions: approx. 98 cm by 72 cm by 16 cm.

Phys. Teach. **24**, 516-518 (Nov. 1986)

Fig. 2. Center and outer beam patterns.

and the large convex and concave acrylic lenses are commercial items available from Klinger Educational Products Co.[1] The rotating mirror assembly is a component of a surplus item obtained from Herbach and Rademan.[2] Most other materials were essentially off-the-shelf or in-house items. The frame is made from 1-in by 6-in solid birch, and the back is 3/4-in plywood. The front side of the back is covered with matt-white projection screen material for reflection enhancement. Grooves were cut in the frame so that the back is 2 cm from the wall. This provides space for the connecting wiring from the external power supply to the projectors and switch and still allows the frame to fit flush against the wall. Wiring is routine. A groove was also cut near the front of the frame to accommodate the 1/4-in thick acrylic cover. This cover has four 6.5-cm-diam finger holes for access to the projector knobs. The rotating mirror assembly is mounted on the front cover. The inside of the frame is lined with single-strength glass mirrors on all sides except the one next to the projectors.

The top and bottom wooden mounting brackets serve to secure the portable unit to the wall; the top bracket is easily removable so that the unit can be moved to the classroom with little effort. Each of the bulbs in the projector is 55 W; the temperature in the enclosure never exceeded 54°C. Optimum viewing is achieved in nearly total darkness, but general viewing is possible with subdued lighting.

Representative Beam Pattern

Fig. 2 shows the center or fixed beam, along with the two outer variable-angle beams, for each projector. The center beams of the multiple-ray projectors do not have a direction change capability. The lower center ray is shown passing through the plano convex lens, beam splitter, and the transmission-reflection filter. The filter reflects red light and transmits blue light. The upper projector center beam is shown passing through the concave lens, through one of the "twisted" prisms, and then incident on the rotating mirror unit.

The two broad diverging beam patterns on each side of the upper projector center beam are the colorful, first-order images from the diffraction grating placed directly in front of the center beam just as it leaves the projector hous-

Interactive Physics Demonstrations

ing (see Fig. 2).

With all rays set parallel to the axis of each lens, diverging and converging effects are clearly shown. By varying the angles of the beams and manipulating the rotating mirror, the number of patterns is limited only by the imagination.

Final Remarks

This unit has been in use for approximately one year. Fig. 3 shows the author with the unit. The unit is mounted on a wall toward the end of a main classroom corridor where traffic is at a minimum and the lighting can be controlled. Students and visitors frequently go out of their way to operate and experiment with the display unit. They are usually fascinated with the effects and appreciate its educational and teaching value.

References

1. Klinger Educational Products Corporation, 83-45 Parsons Blvd., Jamaica, NY 11432.

2. H & R Corporation (A Herbach & Rademan Company), 401 E. Erie Ave., Philadelphia, PA 19134.

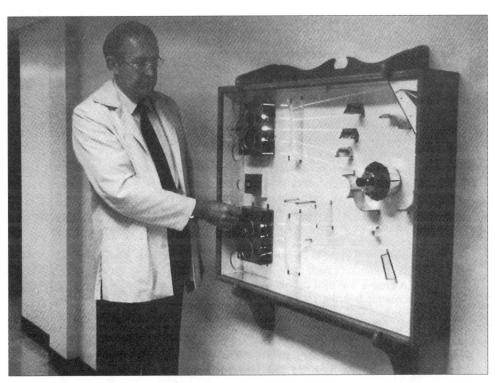

Fig. 3. Author with demonstration unit.

Ray Optics Corridor Demonstration

Ralph B. Knollenberg, Physics Department, University of Louisville, Louisville, KY 40292

We have found that the use of He-Ne lasers to demonstrate ray optics is more effective than the use of classical light sources.

An apparatus using two lasers is depicted in Fig. 1. The mounting board is two meters long and is made of 3/4-in plywood, painted with flat white paint, and supported with wooden feet. The optical components may be familiar to you as the Klinger #K04100 Blackboard Optics Kit. Each optical component is provided with a 1/4-in by 20-in stud and wingnut so that it can be easily mounted on the board by inserting the stud through an appropriately located hole in the board and securing the component there with a wingnut. The mounting technique allows rotation of the optical component when desired.

The lasers are mounted to the board with 1/4-in by 20-in studs, crossbars with rubber feet, and wingnuts.

Phys. Teach. **19**, 563 (Nov. 1981)

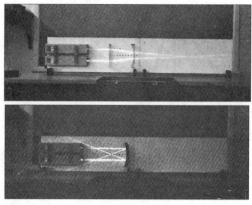

Fig. 1.

To make the rays visible, a cylindrical lens having a short focal length is used to form a sheet of light perpendicular to the plane of the board. A short piece of 8-mm diam Pyrex cane serves as the lens. It is mounted on the laser with beeswax.

The author is grateful to Ordie I. Deats, our instrument maker, who did the machine work necessary to prepare the apparatus.

A Corridor Demonstration for the Minimum Angle of Deviation[1]

Wallace A. Hilton, William Jewell College, Liberty, MO 64068

To help students better understand the concept of the minimum angle of deviation and how to measure it,[2-4] a corridor demonstration may be prepared to show the changing angle of deviation as the prism of the spectroscope is effectively "rocked" back and forth by a 4-rpm electric motor. The spectrum is focused on the screen and as the prism is rotated it is easy to identify the minimum angle of deviation.

Two prisms are used in the demonstration: one of crown glass and the other of flint glass. A single filament showcase-type bulb serves as a single-slit light source. It is housed in a metal case with a lens to focus the images on the screens. A beam splitter directs half of the light through each of the two prisms and onto the screens where the spectra are observed to be moving toward and away from the minimum

Phys. Teach. **16**, 242-243 (April 1978)

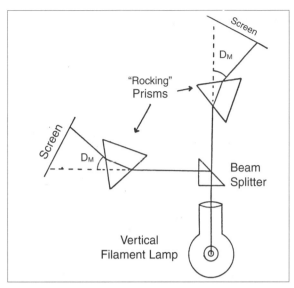

Fig. 1. A schematic arrangement of apparatus to demonstrate minimum angle of deviation of light through a prism.

Fig. 2. Small rigid wires mark the minimum angle for each of the prisms, which are mounted on tables and are "rocked" through about 40° by motors each 15 s. As the prism rotates, the spectrum is observed to approach the minimum angle of deviation and then to recede from it.

angle of deviation. The arrangement of this equipment is shown in Fig. 1 and a photograph of it is shown in Fig. 2. When used as a corridor demonstration, a push button starts the "rocking" of the prisms and the minimum angles deviation for the two prisms are observed on the screens. A time switch turns off the motors after three minutes.[5]

A larger scale model of this equipment is helpful as a lecture room demonstration where the spectrum may be projected on a large screen and the minimum angle of deviation observed by the class.[6]

References

1. Exhibited at the AAPT Apparatus Competition, Chicago, Feb. 7-9, 1977.

2. C.N. Wall, R.B. Levine, and F.E. Christensen, *Physics Laboratory Manual*, (Prentice-Hall, Englewood Cliffs, 3rd Ed., 1972), pp. 290-96.

3. V.E. Eaton, M.J. Martin, R.S. Minor, R.J. Stephenson, and M.W. White, The Prism Spectroscope, Central Scientific Co., No. 71990 L52b.

4. H.F. Meiners, W. Eppenstein, K.H. Moore, and J.P. Nickol, *Analytical Laboratory Physics*,(Edwards Brothers, Ann Arbor, 1955), pp. 214-16.

5. W.A. Hilton, "Time Switch for a Corridor Demonstration," *Am. J. Phys.* **31**, 132, 1963.

6. W.A. Hilton, "Large Scale Demonstration of the Minimum Angle of Deviation," *Phys. Teach.* **7**, 513 (1969).

Animated Displays II: Multiple Reflections

Paul Chagnon, Physics Department, University of Notre Dame, Notre Dame, IN 46556

Physics display cases and science museums often include some examples of multiple reflection from plane mirrors. A given exhibit may emphasize geometrical optics or parity changes or even crystalline structure.[1] In the exhibit to be described here, simple animation enhances the understanding of some displays and in others brings out certain aspects that are commonly overlooked. None of the displays is itself original; all of them are at least touched upon in Sutton's classic demonstration book[2] and most have been described even earlier.[3] Only the animation has been added here. The displays in this exhibit consist of sets of single, double, and triple plane mirrors; hinged plane mirrors; and parallel mirrors. The last is only incidentally animated. The use of a passive-infrared motion detector to control exhibits like this one will also be discussed. An earlier article[4] described our main display case and stated some guidelines for animating displays.

Rotating Single, Double, and Triple Mirrors

An arrangement of two plane mirrors set at right angles to each other and meeting at an edge is often called a corner reflector. The three-dimensional version is called a corner cube or cube corner. To avoid confusion between them we call these — along with the ordinary plane mirror — single, double, and triple mirrors. These terms correspond to the number of reflections forming the central image in each.

Of all multiple-reflection displays, the double mirror is the most commonly seen and is either discussed or given as a problem in many current introductory textbooks.[5] Almost invariably the double mirror is oriented with the

Phys. Teach. **30**, 488-494 (Nov. 1992)

common edge vertical. In terms of the central image of the viewer's own face, the two axes that are inverted are the in-out and left-right ones. The image is upright, and since the number of reflections is even, the handedness of the image is the same as that of the object. Viewers "see themselves as others see them." But what if the double mirror were oriented with the edge horizontal? That is much less well known, perhaps because the question is too infrequently asked.[6] The axes that are inverted are in-out

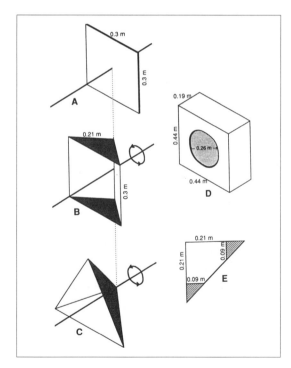

Fig. 1. A, B, C: Single, double, and triple mirrors arranged so that their symmetry axes are parallel and the central images will appear at the same depth. In the exhibit, B and C are attached to real axles behind the mirrors, turned by motors. D: Approximate dimensions of the enclosures that frame the images to avoid excessive overlap. E: Dimensions of the three mirror pieces that make up triple mirror C. The long points in C serve little purpose and are omitted.

Fig. 2. Single, double, and triple mirrors in their enclosures. The photographer's _right_ hand is holding a cable release. Since the double mirror is turned about 60° from the vertical-edge position, the image is rotated about 120°. It is right-handed. In the triple mirror, the image is reversed in all directions and does not move as the mirrors turn.

and up-down, so the image is now upside down. Handedness is unchanged, since this depends only on the number of reflections. How does the image turn upside down? When the double-mirror assembly rotates about an axis bisecting the normals to the mirrors (Fig. 1B), the central image rotates about the same axis through twice as great an angle. In particular, turning the mirrors through 90° rotates the image by 180°. Actually seeing the image turn over is startling when the object is the viewer's own face (Fig. 2). In our display, the double mirror makes a 90° turn in a few seconds and pauses for about 10 s in both the vertical and horizontal orientations, so that the viewer may compare those two cases.

The triple mirror, or corner cube, is mentioned in several of the same textbooks, or it is left up to the reader to extrapolate from two dimensions to three. Attention is usually directed to the retrodirective property of this arrangement, but little or nothing is ever said about the appearance of the central image. If you place a small, well-made triple mirror somewhere in plain sight in a classroom, sooner or later it will literally catch everyone's eye. Each viewer eventually notices that the image at the center of the triple mirror is that of an eye, and in fact an image of his or her own eye.[7] This is a direct consequence of the retrodirectivity. (In the double mirror, the pupil of the viewer's eye will be imaged somewhere on the common edge, but not necessarily in the field of view.) In our display, the triple mirror is large enough to show the viewer's whole head, always with the eye's pupil at the apex of the three mirrors. By the three reflections that form the central

image, all of the spatial axes are inverted, so the image is always upside down, facing the viewer, and of the wrong handedness. Considering the unanticipated effect of rotating the double mirror, it is natural to wonder what happens when the triple mirror rotates about its axis of threefold symmetry, the line making equal angles with all three planes (Fig. 1C). But three inversions are three inversions irrespective of the orientation of the mirrors, so the image does not change in any way, even as the mirrors that form it turn. More technically, inverting the three Cartesian coordinates of every point has the same effect, irrespective of the orientation of the axes. That this is so needs to be seen to

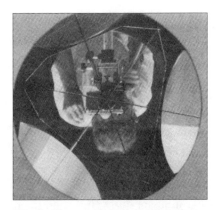

Fig. 3. Close-up of the triple mirror. Three double-reflection images are visible around the central image. These and the three single-reflection images farther out are kept fairly distinct by the framing effect of the enclosure. The central image reflects the center of the camera lens necessarily at the apex of the mirrors. The right-handed photographer is reversed in all spatial dimensions.

Interactive Physics Demonstrations

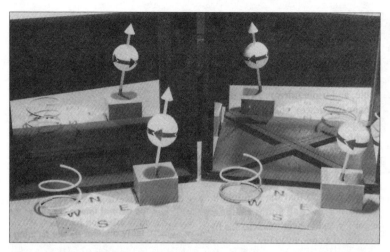

Fig. 4. Stationary single and double first-surface mirrors, each with a compass card, a helix, and a model "neutrino" as objects. The axis of the latter is attached to a small 10-rpm motor that turns the neutrino, and of course its image, in the appropriate direction.

Single and Double Mirrors with Rotating Objects

Plane mirrors are often used to illustrate the effect of odd or even inversions on chirality.[8,9] Since the set of rotating mirrors just described is not well suited for this, our exhibit includes another set of stationary single and double mirrors, seen in Fig. 4. These are made of good quality first-surface mirrors[10] about the same size as the rotating ones. The enclosures are considerably smaller and have open fronts, but again the single mirror is set back so that its plane coincides with the common edge of the double mirror. These are placed below eye level on the floor of the display case, and in front of each one are identical sets of objects including a compass card, a section of helical spring, and a model "neutrino." The latter is a Styrofoam ball with a wooden-dowel "vector" passing through the poles, suggesting velocity or momentum, and a band of directional arrows around the equator suggesting rotation or angular momentum. Signs invite the viewer to compare the images in the single and double mirrors with each other and with the objects themselves.

Experience with an earlier presentation of this display indicated that many viewers stare for a few seconds without getting the point, unless they already know about parity or chirality. The situation improved considerably when the "neutrinos" were mounted directly on small gearhead motors[11] turning at about 10 revolutions per minute.[12] To the uninitiated, actual rotation has more immediate significance than arrows do. Once the viewer notices the counter-rotating "neutrino" images, the compass card and the helix may take on added meaning. It would probably be worth adding a little animation to other objects also; for example, the principal points on the compass cards could be lighted in sequence.

be fully appreciated. The viewer who is close enough also sees, around the stationary central image, three double-reflection images rotating at twice the angular speed of the mirrors, and three single-reflection images whose positions rotate with the mirrors (because the individual mirrors do not rotate about their own normals).

Figure 1 gives the geometry and approximate dimensions of a set of single, double, and triple mirrors large enough to image the viewer's head and to spare. It is important to provide the single mirror, which does not actually rotate, for purposes of comparison. Equally important are the enclosures (Fig. 1D). These serve to frame each image of the viewer's face, so that the multiple images do not overlap much. With the enclosures, the viewer tends to see first the central image, as in Fig. 3, without being immediately distracted by the others. Otherwise, the many images of the viewer and the background are quite confusing for the casual visitor who, of course, does not know what to look for. As the dashed line in Fig. 1 indicates, the plane of the single mirror and the edge of the double one are positioned at the same depth within their enclosures as the apex of the triple one, so that all their central images appear at the same distance from the viewer. The backs of the enclosures support the rotating mechanisms. Further construction details are given in another section.

Hinged Mirrors

The double mirror, or corner reflector, is a special case ($\theta = 90°$) of two plane mirrors joined at one edge with an arbitrary dihedral angle θ between them. This case forms a central image by double reflection and two single-reflection images. The case next most commonly illustrated is $\theta = 60°$, which makes five images by one, two, and three reflections. There is a "well-known rule"[13] that the number of images is equal to $n - 1$ (or the total number of items seen, including the object itself, is n) if the ratio $360°/\theta$ has the integral value n. In a letter, Gladys F. Luhman[14] has stated matters precisely: "The [rule] holds in one or the other of two special cases. For n odd, [it] holds only for an object on the centerline. For n even, for any object position, $(n - 1)$ is the number of separate images formed. (The total number is n, but two of these coincide.)" But this works in a curious way: as θ decreases continuously, two new images appear each time $360°/\theta$ passes through an odd integral value, while at an even integral value, two of the images merge into one and then separate again. For example, if $360°/\theta$ is *either* slightly greater or slightly less than 4, there are four images, but at exactly 4, there are three. If θ decreases until the ratio is 5, there remain four images, so the rule works, but for a slight further increase in ratio the number changes to six images as two new ones appear, simultaneously if the object is on the plane of symmetry. Not all of the images can always be seen from the same vantage point. Nonetheless, if the object is in the right place and one considers only integral ratios, the $(n - 1)$ rule works fine.

Clearly the evolution of images cannot be illustrated in a static display, unless many pairs of mirrors with different angles are used. Our

Fig. 5. The hinged mirrors, stopped at about 50°. The right-hand mirror is raised above the platform to match the height of the wheel on the left-hand one. This provides enough clearance for the crank, directly under the dinosaur, and the crank arm to pass under the mirror frames. The object is raised to about the same height on a Lexan platform. The crank arm attaches under the center of the left or movable mirror. One of the three microswitches that interrupt the motion is visible at right front.

department has had for a very long time a set of hinged mirrors made as described by Sutton.[2] The mirrors are of plate glass about 0.25 by 0.5 m, backed by heavy plywood, edged in brass, and joined at one edge by a sturdy piano-type hinge. The pair is intended to stand on a table, and both mirrors have tiny ball casters underneath so that the presenter can easily and smoothly vary the angle between the mirrors. Included with the mirrors is an object in the form of a small Tyrannosaurus holding a lighted bulb in its jaw.[15] If this set is used as a static display, much of the effect is lost, especially the idea that there is a functional relationship between the number of images and the dihedral angle. Here is a case where some elementary animation can compensate for the absence of a human operator.

We set the hinged mirrors on a platform, as in Fig. 5. One mirror is fixed in place, raised slightly above the platform on the blocks, and the other is provided with a single wheel that rolls more easily and is more durable than ball casters. A gearhead motor under the platform

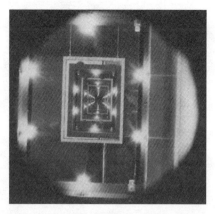

Fig. 6. View through one of the peepholes of the parallel mirrors. The light-colored frame belongs to the mirror through which the camera is looking; the darker frame and the pilot lamps go with the opposite mirror. The peepholes are provided in pairs for stereoptical viewing.

turns a crank just above it that is connected to the movable mirror and drives it back and forth through the range of dihedral angles from 90° (four dinosaurs, including the object) to 30° (12 dinosaurs). The object dinosaur is supported on a Lexan (plastic) subplatform to clear the crank and crank arm. While it would have been feasible, it proved unnecessary to move the object to keep it on the center line, or to move both mirrors symmetrically. One well-chosen fixed object position is satisfactory for this range of angles. On the main platform is a large angle scale marked with the values 360°/n, for n from 4 to 12, so that viewers may compare the number of images with the divisor. The whole arrangement follows the principle that the animating mechanism should be visible whenever possible, but clearly distinct from the demonstration itself. Just one screw attaches the original mirror set to the crank mechanism, and one to the extra wheel.

If the angle changed very slowly, a patient viewer could study evolution and disappearance of images as outlined above. Since this would require more attention than can be expected of the average passerby, we chose instead the same plan as for the rotating double mirror; that is, to use another 4-rpm motor, but to have the motion pause at selected

points. Microswitches tripped by the crank arm interrupt the motion for about 10 s each at the two extremes and at the 360°/7 position.

The hinged-mirror display serves to tie the whole exhibit together. At the 90° position, it becomes a corner reflector. As the angle θ decreases, the number of images increases nearly as $1/\theta$. At $\theta = 0$, the number would in principle be infinite, and we have the parallel mirrors of the next display.

Parallel Mirrors

No exhibit like this would be complete without a pair of nearly parallel plane mirrors (often called "barbershop" mirrors[16]). In most cases, considerable care is taken to fix the mirrors rigidly and accurately parallel. Ours are not so arranged; the two are suspended independently from the ceiling of the display case, about 0.6 m apart, and allowed to sway slightly with the minute air currents and building vibrations. Alternatively, if one mirror is coupled directly to the plate-glass window, modest forces applied to the window will change the angle of that mirror. In either case, small motions are amplified greatly through the multiple reflections. This tends to enhance, rather than to spoil, the perception of looking into an endless tunnel. Both mirrors are first-surface. Each of their frames is painted in a different bright color to make it easier to sort out the images. The front mirror has three sets of peepholes made by etching away the reflecting metal with dilute acid. Six small pilot-lamp bulbs are placed around the periphery of the rear mirror, with their filaments projecting just in front of the reflecting surface. Figure 6 shows a view through one of the peepholes, as a one-eyed viewer would see it through the plateglass window.

Presentation

To accommodate people of different heights, the single, double, and triple rotating mirrors in their enclosures are placed on a shelf that runs across the display case, at a height suitable for a fairly tall man standing close. The shelf is tilted forward by about 15°, so that shorter people, by standing farther away, can also have their faces on the axes of the mirrors. The parallel mirror adjacent to the window has three pairs of peepholes about 0.1 m apart vertically. In addition, a bench about 0.3 m high is placed on the floor before the display case for still shorter people, especially children, to stand on. Beneath these displays, at the bottom of the display case, are arranged the better-quality stationary single and double mirrors with their objects, and the hinged-mirror assembly on its platform.

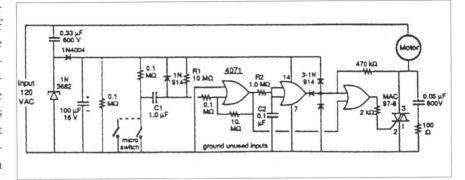

Fig. 8. Diagram of a timing circuit suitable for both the rotating double mirror and the hinged-mirror displays. The three OR gates are on one 4071 chip. One or several normally open microswitches in parallel serve as the input. While the switches are open all the gates are on, and the last of them turns on the small triac. When a switch closes, the first gate shuts off immediately. The second gate stays on for a short time ($\approx$ R2 C2) causing the triac to conduct only on half-cycles. The resulting unidirectional current pulses bring the induction motor to an abrupt stop. After about 10 seconds ($\approx$ R1 C1) the first gate comes on again and motion resumes. Caution: The circuit is not isolated from the power line.

The object for the rotating mirrors is the viewer's face, which needs to be adequately lighted. To this end, a fluorescent lamp is mounted outside the display case on the wall just above its window, shining outward. Other smaller fluorescent lamps concealed beneath the shelf illuminate the objects for the stationary mirrors. The parallel mirrors and the hinged mirrors have their own lighting. Signs leading the viewer to make certain observations, and providing a modicum of explanation, are located near each exhibit. Text for these is given in Appendix 1. The whole exhibit is turned on whenever anyone is in the vicinity by a passive-infrared motion detector whose use is described in Appendix 2.

Some Construction Details

The double and triple rotating mirrors are made from 2-mm-thick mirror tiles from a building-supply store. This proved to be a bad choice because within a year the glass had warped noticeably. It would be better to have a glass shop cut the required pieces (see Fig. 1E) from "single-weight" (3-mm) mirror stock. Of course first-surface mirrors would be preferable, but these are usually made on fairly heavy glass, are expensive and easily damaged. For the rotating mirrors, the nonreflecting seams at the edges where the planes meet are not particularly objectionable. To construct the triple mirror, cement the three sections together with clear RTV.[17] While this is curing, adjust the angles empirically for the best image. After the cement is thoroughly cured, all traces can be scraped off the glass side of the mirrors. The triple mirror will rotate on an axle made of ordinary 13-mm laboratory rod supported on

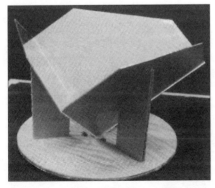

Fig. 7. Triple mirror under construction. The large square at the bottom is the back of the enclosure, to which are mounted the bearings for the axle that supports the plywood disk. The mirror assembly is carefully aligned with the axis of rotation, then props are cemented in place.

two ball bearings. A plywood disk is secured to the end of the axle with a laboratory mounting foot. The disk and axle, prepared in advance, can be set up horizontally as a turntable and the triple mirror placed on it facing up, as in Fig. 7, with a gob of RTV at the center. When the mirror axis has been aligned with the axis of rotation, props made of thin plywood or the like can be cemented in place. After the cement cures, small weights can be added so that the mirror turns easily when the axis is horizontal. A very small motor acting through a double reduction pulley is sufficient to turn the mirror continuously at a few rpms.

Assembly of the double mirror is more straightforward, in that rigid plywood end-pieces fix the two reflectors in place. These and all interior parts of the enclosures should be painted flat black.[18] Because the double mirror starts and stops with each 90° rotation, a positive drive is required. The axle is coupled directly to a 4-rpm gearhead motor, whose output bearing replaces the axle's rear bearing. A simple plywood cam on the axle closes a microswitch at the four positions where the rotation is to pause. The electrical circuit, which is also suitable for the hinged-mirror display, incorporates dynamic braking to stop the motion close to the desired position (see Fig. 8). The three enclosures should not be made until the rotating mirror assemblies are completed, to assure that there will be sufficient clearance inside. These boxes are made from thin (6-mm) plywood except for the backs, which need to be 14-mm or heavier plywood to support the mirror assemblies and drive motors.

References

1. One display of crystal structure by multiple reflection can be seen at Science World, Vancouver, BC, Canada.

2. R.M. Sutton, *Demonstration Experiments in Physics* (McGraw-Hill, New York, 1938), p. 377.

3. For some early examples see Thomas B. Greenslade, Jr., "Multiple images in plane mirrors," *Phys. Teach.* **20**, 29 (1982).

4. P.R. Chagnon, "Animated displays I: Coupled mechanical oscillators," *Phys. Teach* **30**, 275 (1992).

5. Among others: H. Benson, *University Physics* (Wiley, New York, 1991), p. 699; A. Hudson and R. Nelson, *University Physics* (Saunders, New York, 1990), p. 828; H.C. Ohanian, *Physics* (W.W. Norton, New York, 1989), pp. 902-903; R. Wolfson and J.M. Pasachoff, *Physics* (Scott, Foresman, Glenview, IL, 1990), pp. 927-928.

6. T.H. Ansbacher, "The nonreversing mirror with a twist," *Phys. Teach.* **25**, 104 (1987).

7. It is usually the dominant eye; if you close or cover that eye, the image immediately shifts to the other eye. In Figs. 2 and 3, the lens of the camera necessarily occupies the center position.

8. P. Forman, "The fall of parity," *Phys. Teach.* **20**, 281 (1982).

9. E. Hecht and A. Zajac, *Optics* (Addison-Wesley, Reading, MA, 1974), pp. 121-122; I. Galili, F. Goldberg, and S. Bendall, "Some reflections on plane mirrors and images," *Phys. Teach.* **29**, 471 (1991).

10. These mirrors were gleaned from an elementary-particle research project; companies that handle technical surplus materials often offer comparable first-surface mirrors at modest prices.

11. These motors are from American Science Center, Chicago, whose mail-order affiliate is JerryCo Inc., 601 Linden Place, Evanston, IL 60202.

12. A very similar model "particle" can be seen in Fig. 1 of Ref. 8; it is not clear from that photograph whether the model rotates or not.

13. For example, Julius Sumner Miller, *Physics Fun and Demonstrations* (Central Scientific Company, Chicago, 1974), p. 377. The rule is illustrated, but not stated, in D.S. Falk, D.R. Brill, and D.G. Stork, *Seeing the Light* (Harper & Row, Cambridge, 1986), pp. 74-75.

14. Gladys F. Lubman, *Phys. Teach.* **13**, 132 (1975).

15. This dates from an earlier age of monsters, *c.* 1950, not the present resurgence of the dinosaurs.

16. In six decades of visits to barbershops far and wide, the author has yet to find parallel mirrors there.

17. Acronym for **R**oom-**T**emperature **V**ulcanizing silicone rubber, available in tubes at hardware stores in clear, black, and white. A particular brand is General Electric's Clear Household Glue & Seal.

18. Krylon™ Ultra-Flat Black seems to be less reflective than other brands.

Appendix 1: Text of the Signs for this Exhibit

(Rotating double mirror)

When You See This, You'll Flip

What to see and notice:

When the center line joining the mirrors is vertical, your image is upright, but when it's horizontal, your image is upside down. More generally, the image rotates at twice the rate of the mirrors.

What is going on:

You may wish to examine the stationary single and double mirrors below. A single mirror reverses images along the line of sight. The double mirror reverses images, both along the North-South axis, the way you are facing, and also along one other axis. When the center line of the mirrors is vertical, you may not have noticed that left and right are reversed. When it is horizontal, left and right are correct, but up and down are reversed instead.

(Rotating triple mirror)

Why Doesn't Your Head Spin?

What to see and notice:

No matter how the triple mirror turns, North and South, East and West, and up and down are all exchanged. Your image in the mirror is facing you, it is upside down, and its left is on your right. If you look to the side, you can see six other images of yourself. Three rotate like the double mirror one, and three move around the center.

What is going on:

Three mutually perpendicular mirrors acting together reverse images in all three spatial dimensions. Since those are all the dimensions there are, the exact orientation of the mirrors doesn't matter. When you look to the side, you see the images formed by three pairs of two mirrors each, and still farther the "normal" images reflected in one mirror each.

(Parallel mirrors)

On a Clear Day...

What to see and notice:

Look through one set of peepholes. If the mirrors are 0.5 m apart, how far are you seeing? To help you figure out *what* you are seeing, one mirror frame is red and the other is yellow.

What is going on:

Between parallel mirrors, light will be reflected back and forth indefinitely. Each successive image appears smaller than the last because it is farther away. The images become dimmer because at each reflection a few percent of the remaining light intensity is absorbed. The number of reflected lamps you can see is limited because, after a certain point,

the glass bulb in one image blocks the filament in the next one. Since the mirrors are not perfectly parallel, the images form an arc of a circle, and eventually you cannot "see around the curve."

(Stationary single mirror)

Single Mirror

What to see and notice:

Wave one hand in front of the mirror. Is its reflection a right or left hand? Compare the reflected images of the helical spring, the compass card, and the model neutrino (white ball) with the original objects and with the images in the double mirror nearby. Which way is the neutrino's image turning?

What is going on:

In images formed by light reflected once, the orientation of one axis is reversed, the axis perpendicular to the mirror, in this case the North-South axis. (You are facing North.) The other two axes (East-West and up-down) are unchanged. Reversing only one of the three spatial dimensions changes the "handedness" of your hand, of the helical spring, of the compass card, and of the neutrino. Their images cannot be matched to the original objects by any rotation.

(Stationary double mirror)

Double Mirror

What to see and notice:
[Same as stationary single mirror]

What is going on:

There are two mirrors joined at right angles, with the intersection vertical. In images formed by light reflected twice, the orientation of two axes is reversed, in this case the two horizontal axes, in effect North-South and East-West. The remaining (up-down) axis is unchanged. Inverting two of the three spatial dimensions changes "handedness" twice, putting it right. Thus the images of your hand, the compass card, the helical spring, and the neutrino only differ from the originals by being turned around (rotated).

(A separate sign)

Reflections on Parity

Until 1956, most physicists believed that, in any fundamental interaction, there could be no preference between an event and its mirror image. Under this assumption of "parity" or "parity conservation," a radioactive nucleus cannot emit *predominantly* electrons whose direction of spin bears a definite relation to their direction of travel, since this is a "handedness" relationship that would be reversed upon one or three reflections.

That this does in fact occur is now well known, along with many other "violations of parity conservation." This particular "violation" is related to a definite handedness attributed to the neutrino accompanying the radioactive (beta-) decay process.

(Hinged mirrors)

Is This How Dinosaurs Multiplied ?

What to see and notice:

Count the images of the dinosaur when the angle between the mirrors is 360°/4 = 90°, when it is 360°/12 = 30°, and when it is 360°/7 ≈ 51°. Do you see a connection between the number of dinosaurs and the divisor?

What is going on:

If 360° is evenly divisible by the angle between the two plane mirrors, then the quotient should equal the total number of dinosaurs that you see, counting the original object as one. Those images that result from a single reflection are themselves reflected by the other mirror, and so on, to make that number. When the angle is 90°, the effect is the same as the two mirrors fixed at right angles, to your left. When the angle is 30°, there are 12 dinosaurs to be seen, 11 of which are reflected images (you also see a large number of fainter images due to reflection in the glass of the window). In the case of the "parallel" mirrors at your upper right, the angle between the mirrors is made as small as possible, so the number of images, according to this rule, is very large, yet you can notice that, just as here, the images all lie on an arc of a circle. The center of that circle is on the line where the planes of the mirrors intersect (the hinge).

Appendix 2: Use of a Motion Detector

To reduce wear and show some concern for energy conservation, the whole display action and lighting for this exhibit are initiated through a passive-infrared motion detector mounted inconspicuously in the region outside the display case. These are sold as burglar protection devices at hardware and discount stores, often packaged with two floodlight holders. Such a motion detector responds to minute changes in the flux of radiation at a wavelength of the order of 10 μm, as occurs whenever a person ($T \approx 300$ K) enters its field of view. Not only is a motion detector much easier to set up than a photoelectric-cell arrangement, but each one incorporates an updating timer. That is, power remains on for as long as there is activity in the area and for an adjustable period of time after the last disturbance. This avoids frequent on-off cycling. The motion detector may be permanently wired into the mains supplying the display case, with a switch provided to bypass it as needed. There is one catch: motion detectors sold for household burglar protection are designed not to work in the daytime. It turns out that this is arranged through a separate photoresistor that responds to visible light. To

Fig. 9. Circuit board of a typical motion detector. The pencil is pointing to a photoresistor that disables the unit in visible light. To use the detector in daylight, mask the photoresistor with black electrical tape, or remove it. Do not touch the infrared detector, which is the larger shiny object just beneath it. Adjustments for sensitivity and duration can be seen at the bottom of the picture.

use one of these in a lighted room, it is merely necessary to locate the photoresistor and cover it with black tape (see Fig. 9). Of course it is possible to purchase motion detectors without this feature, but the hardware store kind is cheaper and easier to obtain.

Shadow Kaleidoscope

Joe Pizzo, Department of Physics, Lamar University,
Beaumont, TX 77710

This exhibit is a rough copy of the one at the Exploratorium.[1] Nevertheless, its description here seems timely in view of the delightful article on kaleidoscopes by Jearl Walker in a recent issue of *Scientific American.*[2] Walker points out that the traditional kaleidoscope contains either two or three reflecting surfaces making a "V" or a triangle, respectively. The shadow kaleidoscope consists of two reflecting surfaces making an adjustable angle. Multiple images are created from the shadows cast by a participant's fingers (see Fig. 1).

Front surface mirrors would be most desirable for this exhibit, but we have found that good quality rear surface mirrors, purchased from a department store, are acceptable. Our mirrors are approximately 13 cm by 18 cm. They are adhered to blocks of 3/4-in plywood of the same dimension. The plywood blocks are hinged together at the back with a leather strap and wood screws. This hinge allows the mirrors to make a minimum angle of approximately 50°. One of the plywood blocks can be secured to a platform to keep one mirror in a fixed position. A stop can be placed behind the other mirror to allow a maximum angle of 90°. (For larger angles, the images are not too interesting.)

We have found that the lighting is the most critical ingredient for the success of this exhibit. The mirrors must be illuminated from *directly* overhead by a relatively bright source (we use a bare 150 W bulb). The participant's eyes should be shielded from this light. (We use a heavy dark cloth, shown in the upper portion of Fig. 2.) Finally, the whole exhibit should be placed in an area of low-level illumination. (We removed the fluorescent tubes in this section of the hallway.)

This is one exhibit where graphics are absolutely necessary. The easiest way to instruct the participant in the operation of the shadow

Fig. 1. Multiple images can be created from the shadows of a finger or thumb in the Shadow Kaleidoscope.

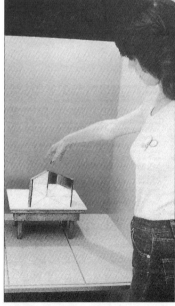

Fig. 2. The Shadow Kaleidoscope is placed directly below a bare 150 W bulb. The bulb is shielded from the participant's eye by a heavy dark cloth.

kaleidoscope is to post photographs similar to Fig. 1, with the invitation to "create your own patterns."

References

1. R. Bruman, *Exploratorium Cookbook* (The Exploratorium, San Francisco, 1975), pp. 20.1-20.2.

2. J. Walker, *Sci. Am.* **253**, 134 (1985).

Phys. Teach. **24**, 237 (April 1986)

An Interactive Soap Film Apparatus

Chris Chiaverina, Barrington High School, 616 West Main St.,
Barrington, IL 60010

In less than an hour, you can build a large-scale soap film demonstration apparatus that is both educational and entertaining. The device, which was inspired by an exhibit at the Exploratorium in San Francisco, may be assembled almost entirely from PVC pipe. Used with a soap bubble mixture of dishwashing detergent and water,[1] the device will enable you and your students to produce rectangular soap films approximately 1 m wide and 2 m high. Blowing on the rectangular film results in bubbles that must be seen to be believed (Fig. 1)!

The availability of hardware, low cost, and ease of construction are additional features that make this apparatus attractive. All components can be found at hardware or building supply stores for about $20.

Construction

The elements used to construct the device are shown in Fig. 2, and the completed apparatus is shown in Fig. 3. The framework is formed from 2.54-cm (1-in) PVC pipe. The 2-m vertical support pipes are secured to a wooden base using two PVC adapters and two metal flanges. Two PVC elbows are used to attach the l-m-long top section of the frame to the vertical support pipes. Although the pieces can be cemented together with PVC cement, assembly that relies on friction alone seems to be sufficient and allows for easy disassembly of the apparatus.

A plastic planting box serves as the bubble solution tank. One piece of 1.3-cm (1/2-in) and one piece of 2.5-cm (1-in) PVC pipe were cut to fit lengthwise along the bottom of the plastic box. The 2.5-cm pipe section is used as an anchor in the bottom of the box, while the 1.3-cm piece acts as the movable rod used to form the soap film. A metal rod, inserted in the anchor pipe, adds mass to the pipe and keeps it from moving. The movable rod is guided by two lengths of fishing leader that pass through holes drilled in the rod. The fishing leader is stretched taut between the top section of the frame and the 2.54-cm (1-in) anchor pipe in

Fig. 1. Spectacular bubbles may be produced by blowing on the rectangular soap film.

Phys. Teach. **26**, 238-239 (April 1988)

the box. A rope attached to the center of the movable piece of PVC pipe passes over a small pulley connected to the center of the top section of the frame. A soap film is produced by pulling on the rope, retracting the 1.3-cm pipe from the bubble solution.

Operation

The soap film demonstration apparatus, which is now found in many interactive science museums, has a variety of uses. It may be used to explore the properties of thin films and thin-film interference. The colors produced by the changing thickness of the soap film are beautiful, and their evolution is fascinating to watch. Two-dimensional waves also can be investigated. Blowing on the film produces large-amplitude ripples. In fact, with a little practice, standing waves can be produced by blowing on the film or by shaking the device at the right frequency. Students and teachers have fun either way, watching the swirling film or by blowing spectacular bubbles!

The apparatus may be used as a corridor or teacher-centered demonstration, a part of a phenomenological laboratory on interference, or an exhibit in an interactive museum. Currently our device is sitting on a laboratory table near the door in the physics room. Without fail, students entering or leaving the room stop to blow some bubbles.

At the beginning of the year, the support pipes were shortened so that the device would fit inside our display case. A cord passed through an opening in the top of the case allowed people to form their own sheets of film. Even though this arrangement did not allow bubble blowing, it still proved to be an engaging exhibit. Whatever the setting, it's a good bet that this piece of apparatus will stimulate your students!

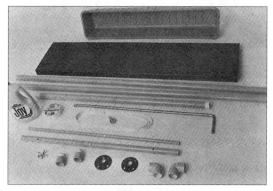

Fig. 2. Readily available materials are used in the construction of the soap film apparatus.

Fig. 3. The soap film apparatus in use.

Reference

1. There are many bubble recipes. A simple and inexpensive bubble solution can be made from one part dishwashing detergent and six parts water. "Joy" and "Dawn" seem to be good detergents to use. A more involved solution, supposedly capable of producing more tenacious bubbles, was recently described in a local newspaper article on "bubbleology." This recipe suggests mixing a quart of "Dawn" with 2.5 gal of distilled water. To this mixture a cup of glycerin is added. Although this solution may produce superior soap films and bubbles, it is more expensive and difficult to clean up. Your best bet is to experiment.

Mixing Colors in the Hall

Cruse Melvin and Timothy Melvin, Department of Physics, Lamar University, Beaumont, TX 77710

Almost 10 years ago this column carried the description of an enticing educational hallway exhibit on color mixing through use of spinning discs.[1] We offer here a somewhat simpler approach to color mixing that is not only inexpensive and portable, but also allows intrusion by the observer into the illuminated area.

Construction

First build a triangular frame with a top ("ceiling") and bottom ("floor"). A ceiling-to-floor height of about 100 cm works well. Attach each of three inexpensive light fixtures to the ceiling (at each apex of an equilateral triangle) with a center-to-center spacing of about 40 to 50 cm. Illuminate the structure with 25-W "crystal" party bulbs in red, green, and blue, which you will find at most variety stores. Wire a dimmer switch to each fixture, mounting each dimmer to the side of the frame adjacent to its associated fixture (see Fig. 1). Put white poster board on the floor of the frame to act as an imaging screen. Hang an object on a string from the center of the illumination triangle. We found a 6-oz disposable cup preferable to a tennis ball because of shadow shape and size. Adjust the hanging object to the optimum height for giving adequate shadow overlap and good viewing of all shadow parts (see Fig. 2). Drape the whole frame with inexpensive heavy black fabric. Then cut an inverted T in the side (about 20 cm across the bottom and 40 cm high). This creates a viewing port when the loose fabric flaps are opened. Place a power switch that will activate all three fixtures close to the viewing port. Set the apparatus on a table of suitable height for convenient viewing.

Fig. 1. Color-mixing apparatus.

Fig. 2. Color-mixing pattern produced by balanced illumination.

Phys. Teach. **33**, 292-293 (May 1995)

Operation

With illumination from three primary color lights equilaterally spaced well above the screen, white is produced on the floor screen. A standard additive color pattern[2] is generated by shadows from the cup suspended below the lights. Three overlapping shadows cause the color mixing. Using the dimmer switches, an observer mixes the colors produced by the three bulbs (red, blue, and green). When the user looks inside the shrouded frame through the viewing port, the pattern appears black in the center where all three shadows overlap (no light hits the screen). The pattern appears as a primary color where any two shadows overlap (only one light hits the screen, producing red, green, or blue). The pattern appears as a complementary color where only one shadow appears (two lights hit the screen, producing yellow, cyan, or magenta). The remainder of the screen continues to appear white. Each light's intensity is regulated by its dimmer switch, which allows the observer to experiment. The user can watch the green shadow as the red light is turned off. The average user will be confident that the green shadow has changed color, even though it did not, demonstrating that the average eye has a response to color that is dependent on the surrounding colors. Detailed discussions of color and color perception are given in texts from the conceptual level[2] through senior optics.[3]

Comments

This apparatus can be used with normal room light. A dimly illuminated area provides better viewing, but some exterior light is needed. We use a wood frame and staple the fabric to it. This makes the color bulbs, which students covet for their rooms, a little less accessible! Put the instructions and/or explanations in an obvious place and definitely mark the color of the bulb by each dimmer switch.

When placed in any hallway, this exhibit will attract students consistently and continuously. We encourage our students to stick their hands inside the port and observe the dynamic shadows created this way.

Acknowlegment

We are indebted to Betty Scott, Hugh Peebles, and Joe Pizzo for assistance and suggestions.

References

1. Richard Bartels, "A hallway display of additive color mixing," *Phys. Teach.* **24**, 564 (1986).

2. Paul Hewitt, *Conceptual Physics*, 7th ed. (Harper Collins, New York, 1993), p. 473.

3. Eugene Hecht, *Optics*, 2nd ed.(Addison-Wesley, Reading, MA, 1987), p. 115.

A Hallway Display of Additive Color Mixing

Richard A. Bartels, Department of Physics, Trinity University,
San Antonio, TX 78284

Some of the walls in our department's hallways consist of large, glass-covered display areas. We have used these for several hallway displays, one of which is a color-mixing exhibit using spinning discs. This exhibit is eye catching and colorful and has been popular among persons using the hallway. When the discs rotate, they undergo an apparent change in color which proves to be quite striking.

The basic idea involved is very simple. For example, if a disc consisting of blue and green segments is rotated rapidly enough, the eye cannot distinguish between the two colors and reacts as if it were being excited by simultaneous beams of blue and green light: that is, a blue-green, or cyan, disc is seen. Likewise, a

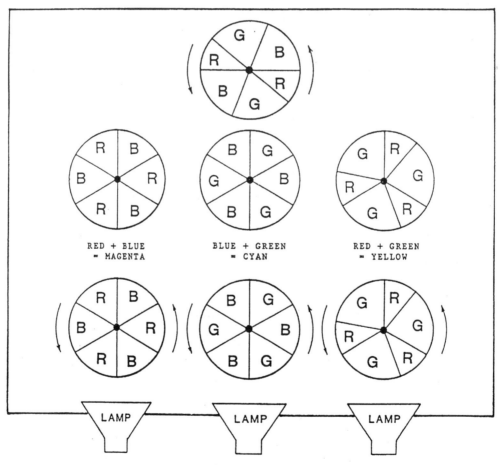

Fig. 1. A diagram of the color-mixing display. Overall size is about 1.3 by 1.3 m. The upper disc and the three lower discs are attached to motor shafts. A switch in the hallway allows the observer to put these four discs into rotation. Another switch in the hallway controls the illumination of the display. The radial segments of the discs are brightly colored: R = red, G = green, and B = blue.

Phys. Teach. **24,** 564-565 (Dec. 1986)

Fig. 2. A photograph of the color-mixing display.

white paint, and then the colored segments are brushed on using fluorescent poster paints. The top disc and the three lower discs can be rotated, while the middle three discs are stationary. The stationary discs provide a reference so the observer can compare the appearance of moving and nonmoving discs. The rotating discs are attached to motors which are activated, all four at once, by a momentary push-button switch in the hallway. A wide variety of motors would work; the ones used here are 110-V AC, 50-W, 1660-rpm drive motors taken from old reel-to-reel tape recorders. A single motor and a belt-pulley system should also work. The display is illuminated with three 75-W flood lamps activated with a time-switch: a button in the hallway, when pushed, powers the lamps for about two minutes. The background of the display is painted flat black.

The upper red-green-blue disc is somewhat disappointing in that, upon rotation, it appears a light gray instead of white. The closest approach to white was found with the red-green-blue area ratios indicated by the upper disc in Fig. 1. Also, with the bright fluorescent colors used, it was found that the best yellow occurred when there was about twice as much green area as red area on the disc (see Fig. 1).

The display is heavily used but has proven to be quite trouble free. In eight years of use, the only maintenance required has been the replacement of one of the flood lamps.

spinning red and blue disc will appear magenta, a spinning red and green disc appears yellow, and a spinning red, blue, and green disc should appear white.

Fig. 1 is a diagram of the display and Fig. 2 is a photograph of it. The discs are 33 rpm, long-playing phonograph records (about 30 cm in diam). They are first sprayed with flat

Corridor Display of Line Spectra

Dean Zollman* and George Athey, Kansas State University,
Manhattan, KS 66506

The apparatus shown in Fig. 1 is being used to display atomic spectra of gases in a hallway or Activities Center[1] environment. To view the spectra the observer only needs to push a momentary switch. Spectra such as those shown in Fig. 2 are then visible. The room lights were turned out to photograph these spectra but the observer can see the colored lines with the room lights on.

The gas tubes are mounted in the back of a black wooden box. Several centimeters in front of the tubes are acetate sheets of a replica transmission diffraction grating.[2] To keep the grating flat it was placed between two sheets of Plexiglas mounted in front of the tubes. Thus, the grating is always in place; the observer can view and qualitatively compare spectra without adjusting any equipment.

The circuit for each tube consists of a momentary switch, transformer, ballast,[3] and the tube connected as shown in Fig. 3. To complete the apparatus, six of these circuits are connected in parallel. The transformers and ballasts are housed in the box in front of the tubes. The cover over these parts is painted black to reduce reflections from the Plexiglas.

Fig. 1. Apparatus displays spectra in hallway exhibit.

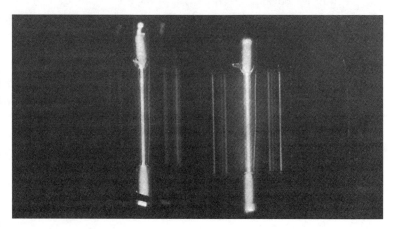

Fig. 2. Examples of spectra seen by observers.

The apparatus, set up in the Kansas State University Physics Activities, was accompanied by a short description of atomic spectra and an offer to lend a spectroscope to anyone who wishes to view other spectra. Each year a few students accept the offer.

Phys. Teach. **15,** 251-252 (April 1977)

References

1. Dean Zollman, *Phys. Teach.* **12**, 213 (1974).

2. Available from Edmund Scientific Co., Barrington, NJ 08007; catalog no. 40,267.

3. Indoor type neon transformer primary voltage 120 V, Secondary voltage 5000 V, available from Jefferson Electric Co., Bellwood, IL; catalog no. 720-361. Single tube fluorescent lamp ballast, Jefferson Electric Co.; catalog no. 234-3041.

---

*   On leave at the American Association of Physics Teachers Executive Office, Graduate Physics Building, SUNY, Stony Brook, NY 11794.

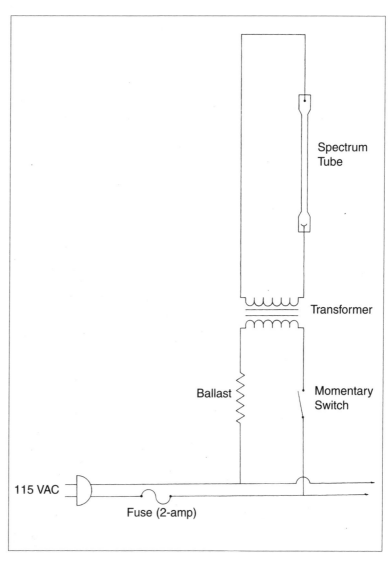

Fig. 6. Electrical circuit used for each of the six gas spectrum tubes.

Animated Displays IV: Linear Polarization

Paul Chagnon, University of Notre Dame, Notre Dame, IN 46556

The detection of linear polarization of visible light is, for the most part, just beyond the unaided perception of our eyes, yet it is responsible for a number of important and visually attractive phenomena. The collection of demonstrations to be described, presented together in a large display case, makes an exhibit well worth a few minutes of the viewer's time. Of course nothing can compare with hands-on experimentation, but when practical considerations preclude that, a little animation can do a lot to help. In all but one of these displays, the animation is simple to produce, requiring nothing more than mounting Polaroid disks on low-speed motors, as others have also done.[1,2] Some details of construction of the various items are given in Appendix I.

An excellent general reference on optical polarization, on a level that is not overly technical, is Frank Crawford's book *Waves*, part of the Berkeley Physics Course.[3] Glynn Davies has described a number of hands-*on* corridor displays[4] that largely overlap the present hands-*off* ones in content, while the realization is quite different. Many other hands-on demonstrations have appeared in this journal and elsewhere.[1,5-8]

Since most light sources emit unpolarized light and human eyes are only slightly sensitive to polarization,[9] it is usually necessary to arrange pairs of devices, one (the polarizer) serving to polarize the light and another (the analyzer) to convert differences in polarization into changes of light intensity. As an exception, birefringence in some cases imparts different directions of travel to components having different polarizations. The distinction between polarizer and analyzer is purely one of function. Anything that analyzes polarized light is equally effective in polarizing unpolarized light.

Some of these displays illustrate the two effects mainly responsible for producing linear polarization in nature, namely scattering and reflection. The effect itself is either the polarizer or analyzer, the other being usually a sheet of Polaroid, which is an artificial dichroic (selectively absorbing) material. The history of Polaroid is well worth reading.[10] Other displays involve effects that change the polarization of the light but do not themselves polarize or analyze. These are sandwiched between two Polaroids. The main examples are birefringence and optical activity (rotation) and their applica-

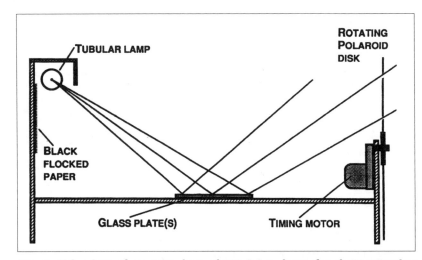

Fig. 1. Side view of an open box, about 0.4 m long, for demonstrating polarization by reflection. At Brewster's angle, the reflected light passes through the center of the exposed upper half of the rotating Polaroid disk. The glass "plate" is actually two or three lantern-slide cover glasses.

Phys. Teach. **31**, 489-499 (Nov. 1993)

tions to stress analysis and to liquid-crystal displays.

Signs placed near each display call attention to the effect featured and offer a simplified explanation (see Appendix II). The following descriptions supplement those.

Polarization by Reflection

That reflection at a transparent surface is polarization-dependent follows from the requirements of continuity of the electric and magnetic field components, the boundary conditions, at the interface. These are implicit in the Maxwell equations.[11] While this is probably the one polarization effect most commonly mentioned in textbooks,[12] there may very well be more students of physics who have memorized the formula for the polarizing angle (Brewster's angle) than have thoughtfully observed the phenomenon itself. An apparatus such as that diagrammed in Fig. 1 brings out the effect very well. This might be considered a miniature and qualitative version of the corridor demonstration described by Smith.[7]

The light source is a clear tubular "showcase" bulb with its straight filament perpendicular to the plane of the drawing, so that the angle of reflection at the horizontal glass plate is well defined for a given position of the viewer's eyes. A stack of two or three thin glass plates constitutes the reflector. Behroozi and Luzader discuss why both surfaces of a plate have the same effective Brewster's angle.[13] The same applies to any number of parallel plates of the same index. The viewer observes the marked variation in the intensity of the reflected light, that is the image of the filament, as the intervening Polaroid disk rotates (Fig. 2). Since the viewer does not need to manipulate the analyzer, he or she is free to concentrate on changing the angle of observation and so to locate the very pronounced minimum that occurs at Brewster's angle.

Polarization by Scattering

In the preceding section we used the effect under study to polarize the light and a rotating Polaroid disk as the analyzer. The alternative, which is usually preferable for a large audience

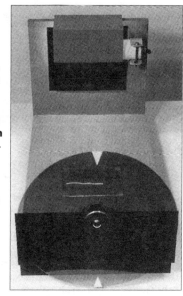

Fig. 2. At right, looking into the reflection apparatus near Brewster's angle. The image of the lamp filament is dimly visible in the reflector. The white markers on the Polaroid indicate its transmission axis. When this is not nearly vertical as shown, the reflection is quite bright.

Fig. 3. Below, cross-section drawing of the scattering apparatus, looking into the light beam. The observer, at some distance to the right, sees simultaneously the direct view of the side of the tank and the reflected view of the top. The tank is about 0.25 m wide and deep, and 0.75 m long.

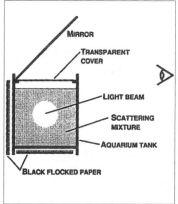

or in a display case, is exemplified here. A collimated beam of light passes first through a slowly rotating Polaroid disk, and the subsequent Rayleigh scattering serves as the analyzer. The visual effect then is that the glow of scattered light brightens and dims as the initial polarization direction changes. Yet the beam intensity itself doesn't change at all, as the viewer can observe by looking at the screen beyond the scatterer. A mirror is arranged, as in the drawing of Fig. 3, so that light scattered into two perpendicular directions can be monitored simultaneously.[14] When it is bright in one view, it is of course dim in the other. The whole setup can be seen in Fig. 4, a photograph taken at an instant when the light beam's polarization was nearly horizontal, so that bright scattering shows up in the mirror while the direct view is

Fig. 4. Rayleigh scattering setup in operation. Light travels from left to right. In this photograph, the light beam is polarized nearly horizontally and little light is scattered toward the camera. In the top view of the tank, as seen in the mirror above it, the beam is much brighter. As the Polaroid rotates, the two views alternate in brightness. Light transmitted through the tank forms an unvarying circular yellow spot on the small screen at the right. Unfortunately it does not show up in the picture due to overexposure.

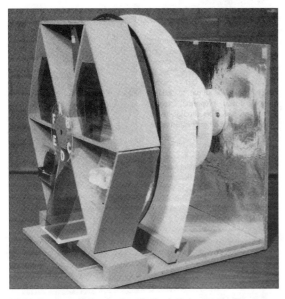

Fig. 5. Arrangement of the six small displays. From right to left are an aluminum reflector, a circular fluorescent lamp, a white Plexiglas diffuser, the large rotating Polaroid, the hexagonal frame with the six displays and, in some cases, individual Polaroid analyzers. The hexagon is about 0.4 m across flats, equal to the diameter of the Polaroid.

almost dark. The scatterer is a suspension of rosin in an aquarium tank about 0.75 m long.

Rayleigh scattering increases markedly with frequency, which accounts for the blue color of the clear sky and the redness of sunrises and

sunsets, depleted of blue light by the same scattering.[15] In live demonstrations with scattering suspensions, it's customary to increase the concentration of scatterer until the transmitted light becomes a pronounced orange-red color, the "sunset" effect. Here that is not possible; the concentration has to be kept low enough to preserve the polarization dependence: The polarizing or analyzing effect is complete only for single scattering at a 90° angle. If too much scatterer is introduced, multiple scattering[16] becomes significant and the contrast is reduced. To compensate for the low concentration, the tank is long enough that a definite change in hue in the scattered light is noticeable from one end to the other, and the residual light on the screen at the end of the tank is yellowish.

To set up this display, the main requirements are, first, a collimated light beam that will not light up the walls of the container and, second, a semipermanent scatterer. A light-beam and polarizer arrangement is described in a later section, and the scatterer in Appendix III. No matter what the material chosen, strict attention should be given to adjusting the amount of scatterer as described in that appendix. Because single scattering is a weak effect, it is necessary that the display be located in dim light, as in a recess within the display case, and especially that it be seen against a dark background. The light beam should not graze the walls of the tank, which makes scratches, dirt, and bubbles light up. Black velvet or other cloth, or black flocked paper, should be arranged behind and beneath the scatterer as well. These materials are superior to black paint.

Small Displays

There are several effects that are best seen when illuminated from the rear by a diffuse source, of course with light that is polarized, and in this application light whose polarization direction is continually changing. We gathered six such displays into a hexagonal frame, each one in a triangular compartment about 0.22 m on a side (Fig. 5). The frame is glued up out of foamboard and painted a dull neutral color.

Behind the whole is a single Polaroid disk, 0.4 m in diameter, mounted on a small timing motor so that it turns constantly at low speed. Behind the Polaroid is a circular fluorescent lamp, with a diffuser of white Plexiglas between them. The compartments are labeled A through F and contain items that illustrate effects that alter the state of polarization. Some are provided with a smaller, fixed Polaroid as analyzer; others (A, C, and E) do not require one. The six displays are not in logical order, but arranged for visual symmetry.

A. Liquid-Crystal Display

Recent articles in this journal describe the workings of liquid-crystal displays (LCD).[17] People are sometimes startled to see their watches go blank when seen through a Polaroid at the appropriate angle, as occasionally happens to wearers of Polaroid sunglasses. We happen to have an LCD clock with large numerals, whose display has been separated from the works so that it can be used on an overhead projector. This was inspired by a similar treatment of an LCD voltmeter described in other articles.[18] This clock occupies compartment A of the hexagon. As the large Polaroid rotates to where it is aligned with the clock's own rear Po-

laroid, 45° from the horizontal in this case, the clock display looks perfectly normal (Fig. 6). When it is perpendicular to that direction, the clock display nominally goes dark (Fig. 7). Actually the effect is even more interesting. The numerals do go dark, the typical dark blue of crossed Polaroids, but they are seen against a still darker background, so the display is inverted from dark-on-light to light-on-dark.

The reason is as follows. Recall that the liquid-crystal assembly includes two Polaroids, one at the front and one at the rear. In the normal use of the clock, as in many LCDs, it is lighted from the front. Light passes through the whole assembly once, is reflected in a small mirror, and passes through again. Because there will be two complete passes, the Polaroid material used in such devices is selected to give higher transmission than the material we use, at the expense of less-complete absorption of the undesired polarization component. Thus when the clock is illuminated from the rear and seen by a single pass of light, the numerals are not as dark as they would normally appear in reflection, though much darker than the background. In the special condition described, however, light entering the liquid-crystal assembly is already polarized at -45°, perpendicu-

Fig. 6. The hexagon of small displays seen from the front. The black tab on the Polaroid, at about the 1:30 position, i.e. +45°, indicates its transimission axis. At this time this coincides with those of the clock (A) and the analyzers in compartments B, D, and F.

Fig. 7. Same as Fig. 6, except that the large Polaroid is now at the -45° position.

Interactive Physics Demonstrations

95

lar to the transmission direction of the LCD's rear Polaroid. It is dimly transmitted, uniformly all over, but has exactly the "wrong" polarization upon entering the liquid-crystal material proper. It follows, then, that the clock will be reversed in appearance, since light passing through the area of the numerals will not be further absorbed, but light passing through the normally clear area will be absorbed again at the front Polaroid.

This reversal effect is not mentioned in the textual material accompanying our display. Fortunately, the few people who ask about it are usually capable of grasping the explanation.

B. Optical Activity

This term applies to situations where the plane of linear polarization rotates progressively around the direction of travel as the light passes through an "optically active" medium such as some sugar solutions, natural turpentine, or crystalline quartz. The light remains linearly polarized at all points, and the rotation is directly proportional to the distance traveled. This should not be confused with birefringent effects (see following). Optical activity occurs in materials having helicity; in the case of certain sugars the molecules themselves are helical, with a predominant handedness, whereas in quartz it is the arrangement of the molecules that is, in a given crystal, either right- or left-handed. Hecht and Zajac give an excellent brief discussion of the subject.[19]

In our display the active material is corn syrup (glucose in water) from the grocery, in a wedge-shaped container. The container is made of a thin (1.5-mm) Plexiglas sheet, solvent-welded by painting the edges with acetic acid. Light passes through a thickness of syrup that increases from about 0 to 50 mm from one side of the wedge to the other, then through a fixed Polaroid analyzer. At the thick end, the polarization direction is turned by about 90°, so for monochromatic light either end can be dark and the other bright, depending on the orientation of the polarizer. But the rotation is in fact highly chromatic. As a rough approximation, the angle of rotation is directly proportional to the frequency of the light. For exam-

ple, if the polarizer and analyzer are parallel and white light is incident, the wedge will be white at the thin end and magenta at the other (where the green component has rotated 90°), with a progression of colors between. Since the polarizer is slowly turning, the net effect is a sequence of colored stripes traveling across the wedge, say from left to right depending on the sense of rotation of the polarizer. Just as in thin-film interference, the colors perceived in this demonstration are determined mainly by the wavelength that is missing from the initial white light, so the subtractive primaries predominate.

C. Calcite

The display consists of some printed text, on a transparent backing, with a cleaved calcite crystal, about 3 cm thick, in front of it. These are in front of the large diffuse light source and polarizer already described. There is no separate analyzer. As the polarizer turns, the part of the printing that shows through the calcite appears double, with a separation of perhaps 2 mm between the images, or either image alone can be seen. What is happening is discussed in most of the textbooks that mention polarization at all. One of the most cogent explanations can be found in Ref. 20.

Calcite is birefringent, meaning that there are different velocities or refractive indices for light whose polarization, or electric field, lies along certain axes determined by the crystalline structure. In simpler examples of birefringence (see part F of this section), the direction of travel and the two directions of polarization that yield the highest and lowest speeds are mutually perpendicular. This is not the case for light entering a cleaved calcite crystal normal to any of its surfaces. The result is that light of one polarization (the extraordinary ray) is deviated even when the angle of incidence is 0°. Upon leaving the opposite face, it will be deviated oppositely, leaving a net displacement. Light of the orthogonal polarization, the ordinary ray, follows the usual Snell's Law. If the incident light is unpolarized, or if its polarization has components that correspond to both the ordinary and extraordinary rays, the two orthogonally polarized components proceed in different directions through the crystal, forming the two images. When the initial polarization corresponds to one or the other ray, only that image is seen.

D,E. Birefringent Plastics

The next two compartments contain common but artificial materials that alter the state of polarization. Mica, once common, is no longer familiar to most people. One is a crumpled-up sample of cellophane (the crinkly stuff; one of the earliest synthetic wrapping materials) and the other is an ordinary small plastic box. When placed between Polaroids, both exhibit colored patterns. For the plastic box, a separate analyzer is not really necessary. The one provided only covers part of the visible area. Colors are seen elsewhere because reflection in the box's surfaces serves as an analyzer. For the inverse reason, people wearing Polaroid sunglasses can see the stress patterns built into the rear windows of automobiles. The cellophane sample requires a Polaroid analyzer.

The long organic molecules in plastics can have some preferential orientation, rendering the material birefringent. In cellophane, the asymmetry is aligned with the length and width of the bulk material from which the sample is cut. Crawford[3] uses cellophane in a number of "home experiments." In the plastic box, the pattern seen appears to relate to the flow of plastic into the mold when the box was formed, being especially prominent near the corners where, presumably, material had to be forced in.[21] The pattern may also be partly stress induced (see "Photoelasticity" section).

A linearly polarized light wave entering a birefringent material can be resolved into components having different polarizations and traveling at different speeds, initially in phase. For simplicity, suppose that these components are perpendicular and have equal amplitudes. Suppose that after traveling some distance the components are recombined. Because of their different speeds, these components will now differ in phase. If the phase difference happens to be 90°, meaning that the *difference* in travel times was ¼ of a cycle, the resultant wave is cir-

cularly polarized, and will show no effect when tested for linear polarization. If the phase difference is 180°, as in a sample twice as thick, the recombined wave is again linearly polarized, but perpendicular to its original polarization, and so on for other thicknesses. Consequently, these materials, when illuminated with light of one wavelength, exhibit patterns of light and dark when placed between two Polaroids.

For light of different frequencies traveling through the same sample, the differences in travel times are about equal, but these translate into unequal phase differences. For example, a time interval that is ½ of a cycle for 350-nm light is only ¼ of a cycle for 700-nm light, whose period is twice as long. This accounts for the colored patterns seen in the demonstration illuminated with white light.

Beneath and in front of the cellophane sample, but behind the analyzer, is placed a small mirror, of the ordinary metal-on-glass kind. The colored pattern seen in the cellophane's image is generally different from that of the sample seen directly. That is, the image of a particular patch of the material appears a different color from that patch itself. This illustrates still another effect, originating in the phase shifts of the parallel and perpendicular components of an electric field when a wave is reflected from an imperfect conductor. In general, metallic reflection will convert linear to elliptical polarization.[3,22]

F. Retardation Plates

The birefringence described for common plastics is, of course, completely irrelevant to their normal purposes. On the other hand, a retardation plate, or retarder, is manufactured or selected to have a specific effect. It is a sample of birefringent material whose "fast" and "slow" axes are parallel to its surface. For normal incidence, the ordinary and extraordinary rays travel in the same direction, though at different speeds. A retardation plate can be cut from an anisotropic crystal such as calcite by sawing it in the appropriate plane. Manufactured retarders of transparent laminated plastic are sold in large sheets, just as is the Polaroid

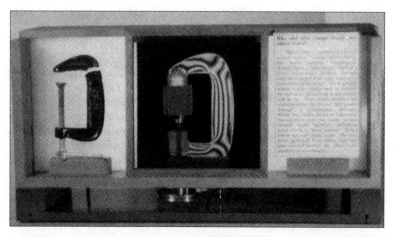

Fig. 8. The broken cast-iron clamp, a slightly larger working-model clamp mounted between crossed Polaroids, and their explanatory sign. The mechanism underneath tightens and loosens the model clamp every few seconds. For this monochrome photograph, the fluorescent backlight was replaced by a bare mercury lamp and a green filter.

letters overlap there is in effect a full-wave plate, restoring the original polarization, so the overlapping parts of the two "dark" letters are bright! When the polarizer has turned to the -45° position, Fig. 7, the background and the overlaps are dark, but the single layers of the letters are bright.

Due to residual effects, "dark" is actually dark blue and "bright" is yellowish. Fortuitously, blue and "gold" are the colors associated with our school, and the overlapping letters ND one of its symbols.

material. Each retarder is designated by the equivalent *difference* in path length for the polarization components of a light wave incident normal to the surface. Thus a "quarter-wave plate" is a retarder for which the time difference equals ¼ cycle, as if one component had traveled ¾ wavelength farther. Such a plate is typically used to convert linear into circular polarization and vice versa. In fact, the plate is very much thicker than ¼ of the wavelength, and both components travel the same distance. A "halfwave plate" changes the orientation of linear polarization by 90°, but the polarization does not rotate continuously as it does in optical activity. Lai et al. have constructed a mechanical analogue of a half-wave retarder.[23]

We cut out large letters "N" and "D" from a sheet of retarder labeled 280 nm, implying that it is half-wave retarder for wavelengths near the middle of the visible spectrum. These letters, one about 15 mm behind the other, occupy compartment F of the hexagon, with a stationary analyzer in front of them. The axes of both retarders are oriented vertically and horizontally, and the axis of the analyzer at 45°. In Fig. 6, when the polarizer is also at 45°, the background is bright, but light that has passed through part of either letter is now polarized at -45°, so that part looks dark. Where the two

Photoelasticity

Materials such as annealed sheets of Plexiglas or Lexan plastic are not normally birefringent, but become so when a mechanical stress is applied. Transparent models of actual structures or machine parts, viewed between Polaroids and under stress, reveal the patterns of stress within those objects.[12,24]

This display has its origin in a cast-iron clamp that broke in actual use. To show why the break occurred at an inside corner, we cut an approximate model of the clamp out of 6-mm-thick Lexan sheet and equipped it with working parts. The broken clamp and the model, between crossed Polaroids, are mounted side by side. A small motor alternately tightens and releases the model clamp, so that the viewer can see the pattern of stress contours build up and associate the existence of the pattern directly with the application of force to the clamp (Fig. 8). This display is self-contained, with a small fluorescent lamp at the rear and, coming forward, a diffuser, a polarizer, the model clamp, and the analyzer. The motor and double reduction pulleys are mounted underneath. A cam on the pulley that turns the screw of the clamp flips a reversing switch at the end of one full turn, following the same general idea illustrated in Fig. 4 of Ref. 25. The original clamp is displayed to one side of the model and an explanatory sign to the other side, all back-lighted by the same lamp.

The "Optical Barber Pole"

In this eye-catching demonstration,[26] both optical activity and scattering are involved. The only new feature here consists of making the whole "barber pole" rotate like a real one, mercly by rotating the initial polarization of the incident light. This does make it all the more mysterious and spectacular. Usually this doesn't go into the display case until several weeks after the rest of the polarization exhibit, so that the display-case habitués have had a chance to absorb some of the earlier lessons. The setup is essentially the same as the basic scattering one above, where a suspension serves as the analyzer for a polarized light beam. Here the light beam is turned vertically upward with a 45° mirror so that it shines through a glass cylinder about 0.1 m in diameter and 0.4 m tall (Fig. 9). The key to this display is the mixture, in this case mainly corn syrup which is optically active, causing the polarization to rotate as the light travels upward, into which is mixed a scattering suspension (Appendix III).

Suppose that as the white light enters the bottom of the column its polarization is perpendicular to the line of sight. Then light is scattered toward the viewer and the bottom of the column looks white. Recall that the rotation is proportional to the frequency as well as to the distance traveled. After a few centimeters, the blue component has rotated by 90°, so blue light is not scattered toward the viewer and the column looks yellow, blue's complementary color. A little farther up, green is the missing component so the column looks magenta, and a little farther the absence of red gives a cyan appearance. The second rotation follows, less distinctly.

Each color forms a left-handed helix. From the viewpoint of an observer above the column looking into the light, the polarization is turning clockwise or "to the right" as the light approaches. This accounts for the sobriquet *dex-*

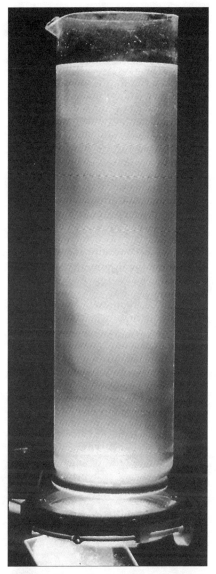

Fig. 9. A linearly polarized light beam shines upward through a cylinder containing the mixture of optically active corn syrup and the scattering suspension, forming the "optical barber pole" explained in the text. The Polaroid disk directly under the column turns slowly, turning the colored helices with it.

trose associated with glucose (the corn syrup). Fructose or *levulose* turns the polarization oppositely, or "to the left." A hypothetical sugar that could rotate the polarization either way equally well would be called, of course, *ambidextrose.*

Appendix I

Some Construction Details

Materials

Polarizers and retarders can be purchased in large sheets, in a variety of forms, directly from Polaroid Corporation.[27] We use the HN-32 polarizer in a laminate 0.75 mm thick. The terminology is explained in textbooks.[3,19] A good selection in smaller amounts is available from Edmund Scientific Company, which also carries a few timing motors and the black flocked paper. Such paper and similar materials may also be had from local art-supply shops. Clear Plexiglas or Lexan, or reasonable substitutes, as well as diffusers, can be found at local plastics distributors or building-supply stores. Any glass shop will cut a mirror to size from single-weight stock. Rosin is carried by music shops. Sheets of mica or cellophane, or old-style clear cellophane tape, can be used as phase retarders.

Fig. 10. Arrangement for producing a collimated beam of white light whose linear polarization rotates.

Light sources

For a collimated light source for the scattering experiment, it may be sufficient to find a slide projector with a long-focus lens (say 200 mm focal length). A more controllable way is to mount an auxiliary lens, with a diameter of the desired beam size, of the order of 75 mm, and a focal length of the order of +200 mm, some distance from the slide projector, which is equipped with a short (75-mm) focal-length projection lens. The exact positions of the lenses can be determined empirically and the space between them can be utilized for the polarizer. Such an arrangement, based on a common type of slide projector, is shown in Fig. 10. A thin aluminum square with a 30-mm round hole punched in it, placed in the slide holder, helps a great deal to clean up stray light at the edges of the beam.

Some slide projectors use two condensing lenses. It may happen that removing one of the two, and removing the projection lens also, results in quite a parallel beam. That is what we used for the "optical barber pole" display.

Both of these slide projectors have had ordinary household solid-state lamp dimmers wired into their lamp circuits only. The light intensity is thus easily adjusted to just what is needed and no more, extending the life of the projection bulbs to several hundred hours of use. Connecting the whole projector including the motor to a solid-state dimmer is definitely contrary to the common wisdom, although Taylor says that it is all right to do so.[28]

Figure 11 shows a simple way to attach a Polaroid disk to the shaft of a timing motor. Disks can be cut from the laminate by repeatedly tracing the desired circle with a sharp tool. Shearing is not advised, since the layers of the laminate may tend to separate. The disks up to 0.25-m diameter stay flat enough for practical purposes without any support. Our largest disk, used with the hexagonal rack, is stiffened by a steel wire rim attached with tape.

Another, more compact way to rotate a Polaroid is to mount it in a ring gear, as in Fig. 12. This is used directly under the "optical barber pole," with the light beam passing right

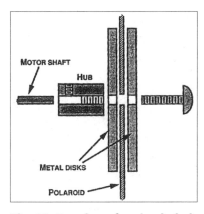

Fig. 11. Drawing of a simple hub for connecting a Polaroid disk to the output shaft of a timing motor.

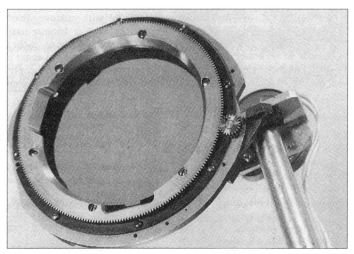

Fig. 12. A Polaroid disk mounted in a ring gear, driven by a faster timing motor, is a more compact way to achieve the desired rotation.

through the center. There is some possibility of overheating the Polaroid in this configuration if the light source does not incorporate a heat-absorbing glass, as slide projectors usually do. The ring-gear assembly, taken from some WWII optical device, just happened to be available. The same general idea could be executed much more simply with a friction-driven equivalent, such as described by Freier and Eaton.[29]

Timing motors are convenient to use, even when the exact speed is unimportant, because they are small, easily available in a variety of speeds, and relatively inexpensive.[30] In selecting the speed to use, bear in mind that you get two cycles of polarization in each revolution. Speeds somewhat under 10 rpm work out well for these displays.

Appendix II

Text for the Displays
General

What Is Polarization?

Light is an electromagnetic wave, composed of electric and magnetic fields. Each of these fields must be perpendicular to the direction of travel of the light, but that doesn't specify the field's direction completely. (Linear) polarization simply denotes the particular direction or orientation that the electric field in a light wave has in a given case. A light wave traveling East to West may be polarized along a North-South or an up-down line, or anywhere between. Television antennas are oriented horizontally (in North America) because the TV waves are horizontally polarized, by convention. Sometimes you see other antennas that are oriented vertically; they may be for CB or police communications or some other purpose where the convention is different. Light waves from the usual sources contain an equal mixture of all possible polarizations. They are said to be *unpolarized*. At a given instant, every light wave has a polarization, but in an unpolarized wave that polarization changes randomly from instant to instant.

What Is Polaroid™ ?

Polaroid is an artificial material invented by Edwin Land around 1927. It completely absorbs light of one particular polarization, transmitting only components perpendicular to that one. The orientation of the transmitted waves is called the transmission axis of the Polaroid. When *un*polarized light enters an ideal Polaroid, the part transmitted becomes completely polarized. When light that is already polarized approaches an ideal Polaroid, it will be transmitted or absorbed according to whether its polarization is the same as or perpendicular to the transmission axis. If it is neither the same nor perpendicular, the component parallel to the transmission axis goes through and the rest is absorbed. Thus a Polaroid can act as an analyzer of polarization.

Polarization by Reflection

What to See and Notice

Look at the light reflected in the glass plate on the floor of this box. Look at it through the large round Polaroid disk. Notice that the reflection brightens and dims as the Polaroid turns. Even the paint on the wood next to the glass plate does the same.

What Is Going On

Light from the bulb contains equal parts of horizontal and vertical* polarization. When that light is reflected from the horizontal glass plate, very little of the vertically polarized part is reflected, so the reflected light is horizontally polarized. That light will then be absorbed by a Polaroid that is set to transmit vertically polarized light. The white arrows on the disk show the polarization that it transmits best. The effect is qualitatively always present in reflection from a nonconductor. For one particular angle (Brewster's angle), no vertically polarized light at all is reflected, so the polarization becomes complete. You can find Brewster's angle for glass by moving your head up and down a bit while watching for extinction of the reflected image.

*Oriented in the vertical plane containing the direction of travel, and perpendicular to it.

Polarization by Scattering

What to See and Notice

Step back a little and look squarely at the light scattered from the large tank. Notice that the brightness of the scattered light varies periodically. Look also at the light coming from the top of the tank, which you can see in the mirror. That light dims out when the other is

brightest, and vice versa. The light that goes through the tank and comes out of the end does not vary at all, but is more yellowish than the light that is scattered.

What Is Going On

The tank contains a very dilute suspension of particles that are bigger than water molecules but smaller than the wavelength of light. When light is scattered at right angles by small particles, it is scattered preferentially in the plane perpendicular to its polarization, and not at all in the direction of its polarization. In this display the incident light is polarized through a Polaroid disk that is slowly rotating. When the incident polarization is vertical, light is scattered horizontally toward you (and away from you also). When the incident polarization is horizontal, it is scattered vertically up and down. The total amount of scattering remains the same, so the intensity of the transmitted light does not vary.

What Else Is Going On

The scattered light from the end of the tank near the source looks bluish, and farther on becomes yellowish; the light emerging from the end of the tank is reminiscent of the setting Sun. The chance of a light wave scattering from a small particle depends strongly on wavelength, being much greater for shorter wavelength (blue) than longer (red) light. That is why the scattered light at first looks bluish. Farther along, much of the blue light has been removed from the originally white beam, so the remainder has a yellow cast to it. The clear sky looks blue for the same reason. The chance of scattering by an air molecule is extremely small, but there are a lot of molecules in the sky. Typically, a light wave from the Sun scatters only once from an air molecule in the sky before reaching your eye. When the Sun is setting (or rising!) you see it through a much longer path in the atmosphere than at midday. Much of the blue light has been scattered away, so you see Sun as orange or yellow.

Effects that Alter Polarization

All six compartments in this display are illuminated from behind through a Polaroid filter that is slowly rotating. The black tab on the filter indicates the direction of polarization that it transmits best. Compartments A, C, and E do not have a second Polaroid; they include their own analyzers. But the main effect displayed in each compartment is one that changes, not produces, polarization.

A. Liquid-Crystal Display

Liquid-crystal displays on clocks and calculators consist of a five-layer sandwich: liquid-crystal material in the center, confined by two thin glass plates printed with conducting but transparent segments, between outer layers of Polaroid. The liquid-crystal molecules align themselves with microscopic grooves in the glass, in such a way as to rotate the polarization of light by 90°. The axes of the two Polaroids are crossed, so incident light that becomes polarized upon entering the cell is rotated in passing through the liquid and is transmitted by the second Polaroid. When a small voltage is applied to a conducting segment of the glass, the liquid in that region ceases to rotate the polarization of the light, so it is absorbed by the second Polaroid, forming a dark segment of a numeral.

B. Optical Activity

Here is a wedge filled with dextrose solution (glucose, or corn syrup). In ordinary liquids, molecules are oriented randomly, canceling out any birefringence. Nevertheless, certain liquids are optically active because the molecules themselves are helical (twisted) in shape. A given substance may have all right- or all left-handed twisted molecules. When linearly polarized light passes through such a substance, its polarization is rotated. Unlike in birefringence, the light remains linearly polarized for any thickness of liquid. The angle of rotation is directly proportional to the thickness and inversely to the wavelength. When the light coming through this wedge is analyzed with a Polaroid filter, certain wavelengths are removed from the original white light at each position, resulting in the colorful stripes.

C. Birefringence in Calcite

The surfaces of this natural crystal are not parallel or perpendicular to those axes for which polarized light has the highest and lowest speeds. The result of this is that light entering the crystal is split into two different directions of travel, according to its polarization. When the two light rays leave the surface opposite the one they entered, each resumes the original direction of travel, but one has traveled a little sideways while in the crystal. Each of the two images that you see is formed entirely by light of one polarization only.

D. (1) Birefringence in Cellophane

Many transparent materials are birefringent or doubly refracting (and many are not). Birefringence means that there are two orientations of polarization, for which light traveling in a given direction will have two different speeds. If the incident light happens to be polarized between these orientations, two components with different speeds will result. When the light leaves the material, the two components will generally be out of phase. For any phase difference other than 0° or 180°, the linear polarization is at least partially lost. If the phase difference happens to be 180°, the light will again be linearly polarized, but perpendicular to its original orientation, so it will be absorbed by a Polaroid oriented parallel to the first one. Light of that particular wavelength is removed from the white light, so a colored patch appears on the cellophane.

D. (2) Metallic Reflection

Notice that the light reflected in the mirror is not extinguished at the same time as the light coming directly from the first Polaroid, and that the reflected image of the cellophane has different patterns from the original. Reflection at a conducting surface, such as the metallic coating on an ordinary mirror, does not of itself polarize or analyze light. However the polarization of already polarized light is altered because of phase shifts that occur in metallic reflection.

E. Plastic Box

Like cellophane, the plastic of this box is birefringent. It appears that its molecules were oriented in particular directions during the forming process. If you look downward at it, reflection in the bottom of the box acts as a polarization analyzer so that you see the effects of birefringence in the other parts. The same would happen if you saw the box in light that was initially polarized by reflection or by scattering, so sometimes one can see such colored patterns without any Polaroids at all.

F. Retardation Plates

Artificially produced birefringent material, available in large sheets of various thicknesses, is used in optical devices. The material that these letters are made of would be designated as half-wave plate. When incoming light is polarized at 45° above the horizontal, the components polarized vertically and horizontally travel at slightly different speeds. After traveling many wavelengths through the plate, one component has gained a half wavelength on the other. Upon leaving the plate, the components rejoin to form a wave that is polarized at -45°, or perpendicular to the original one. After the light has passed through two half-wave plates, the original polarization is restored.

Photoelasticity

Why did this clamp break just where it did?

When force is applied to a transparent (Lexan™) model of the clamp, the model becomes birefringent. Where there is little stress, light of a given wavelength passing through may be changed from (say) vertical to horizontal polarization. For a greater stress, it may change back to vertical, for still more stress back to horizontal, and so on. Thus, stress *contours* are revealed when the altered light passes through a polarization analyzer. When the model clamp is tightened, the contours near the inside corners become close together, indicating great stress in these regions. That's where the real clamp broke. The contours produced from white light appear colored because the effect is dependent on wavelength.

The "Optical Barber Pole"

These colored helices are produced by a combination of optical rotation (see item **B**) and scattering. (See large tank information below.) As light travels upward through this column of liquid, its plane of polarization rotates, making about two complete turns. Whenever light of a particular wavelength (color) has its polarization perpendicular to your line of sight, some of that light scatters toward you. The blue part of white turns more rapidly than the red part, causing the colors to separate.

In this display, the *initial* polarization imparted to the light is also made to turn slowly by the motor-driven Polaroid disk just below the column. The liquid is a mixture of corn syrup, for rotation, and a scattering suspension.

Appendix III

Preparation of the Scattering Solutions

In scattering demonstrations, people often use suspensions of milk or similar substances, although these will deteriorate after a few days. Evidently a scattering medium that is easy to make and that keeps well has been the object of several searches.[31] We find the following, the result of experimentation based on a mention long ago by Sutton, to be quite satisfactory.[32]

The objective is to prepare a rosin suspension with a concentration of the order of 10^{-5}, or 10 mg rosin per liter of product. The exact amount should be determined by trial, concentrating on maximizing the contrast between the bright and dark conditions. It is best to proceed in three steps.

a) Dissolve a little rosin in ethyl or methyl alcohol with a low water content, say in the ratio of 20 ml of alcohol per gram of rosin. This will be a clear yellowish solution that keeps indefinitely.

b) Add I part of the clear solution to 100 parts of distilled water. This forms a milky white suspension. There may be some settling out in the first few days, presumably of the largest particles; otherwise this also appears to keep indefinitely. The next step will require on the order of 1 or 2 percent of this suspension in the final scatterer.

c) Have the tank ready and filled with water. Use distilled, demineralized, or at least softened water to avoid eventual mineral deposits. If the water is from the tap, it must stand several hours for the bubbles to clear and any particulate matter to settle. The light source and polarizer must be ready in advance, and the whole display in the setting, and with the lighting, where it will be seen. At this stage there should be almost no visible scattering when the light beam shines through the water. Now add a little at a time of the white suspension, stirring well each time, and observe the scattering at 90°, noting particularly the minimum intensity as the polarizer rotates. At first the minimum should be quite invisible. Increase the concentration of the scattering suspension until the scattering is just barely visible at its faintest. This will give the greatest contrast. With the tank covered to retard evaporation, this scatterer will last indefinitely.

For the "optical barber pole," the viscosity of the corn syrup causes problems in achieving a uniform mixture while avoiding bubbles. The amount of scattering material to use can be determined in advance by setting up the display with plain water rather than corn syrup. The deliberate addition of about 20% water to commercial syrup reduces the viscosity to a more manageable level without greatly impairing the rotation. Arrange a stirrer in the column and add the ingredients (corn syrup, water, and the suspension) in small amounts. Stir as you go, but without entraining air into the mixture. Warming up the whole with a heat lamp further reduces the viscosity, promoting easier mixing and allowing bubbles to escape. The column in the photograph (Fig. 9) contains a mixture prepared four years previously. While in storage, it developed some scum near the surface, but this was easily suctioned off and the missing volume replaced.

References

1. R. Bruman, *Exploratorium Cookbook I* (The Exploratorium, San Francisco, 1975), Recipe No. 26.

2. W.A. Hilton, "An experiment on sky polarization and brightness," *Phys. Teach.* **16**, 294 (1978).

3. F.S. Crawford, Jr., *Waves* (McGraw-Hill, New York, 1968), Chap. 8.

4. G.R. Davies, "Polarized light corridor demonstrations," *Phys. Teach.* **28**, 464 (1990).

5. R. Hipschman, *Exploratorium Cookbook I* (Exploratorium, San Francisco, 1980), Recipe No. 96.

6. R. Hipschman, op. cit., Recipe No. 98.

7. H.A Smith, Jr., "Measuring Brewster's angle between classes," *Phys. Teach.* **17**, 109 (1979).

8. R. Goehmann and S. Welty, "Polarized light: Three demonstrations...," *Phys. Teach.* **22**, 307 (1984).

9. D.S. Falk, D.R. Brill, and D.G. Stork, *Seeing the Light* (Harper & Row, New York, 1986), p. 354.

10. E. Hecht and A. Zajac, *Optics* (Addison-Wesley, Reading, MA, 1975), pp. 228 ff.

11. J.R. Reitz, F.J. Milford, and R.W. Christy, *Foundations of Electromagnetic Theory*, 4th ed. (Addison-Wesley, Reading, MA, 1993), Chap. 18; see also R.K.P. Zia, "Symmetric Fresnel equations: An energy-conservation approach," *Am. J. Phys.* **56**, 555 (1988).

12. D. Halliday, R. Resnick, and J. Walker, *Fundamentals of Physics*, 4th ed. (Wiley, New York, 1993), p. 1017; H.D. Young, *University Physics*, 8th ed. (Addison-Wesley, Reading, MA, 1992), p. 959.

13. F. Behroozi and S. Luzader, "On the reflection of polarized light at surfaces," *Am. J. Phys.* **55**, 279 (1987).

14. R.M. Sutton, *Demonstration Experiments in Physics* (McGraw-Hill, New York, 1938), sec. L-128, p. 424.

15. W.K.H. Panofsky and M. Phillips, *Classical Electricity and Magnetism* (Addison-Wesley, Reading, MA, 1962), Chap. 22; C.F. Bohren and

A.B. Fraser, "Colors of the sky," *Phys. Teach.* **23**, 267 (1985).

16. C.F. Bohren, "Multiple scattering of light...," *Am. J. Phys.* **55**, 524 (1987).

17. C.H. Hayn, "Liquid-crystal displays," *Phys. Teach.* **19**, 256 (1981); A.J. Nicastro, "Demonstrations of some optical properties of liquid crystals," *Phys. Teach.* **21**, 181 (1983); R. Ondris-Crawford, G.P. Crawford, and J.W. Doane, "Liquid crystals: The phase of the future," *Phys. Teach.* **30**, 332 (1992); see also Falk et. al., op. cit., p. 357.

18. M.J. Dresser, "Digital displays for the overhead projector," *Am. J. Phys.* **52**, 379 (1984); P.A. Bender, "Adapting a digital multimeter for use on an overhead projector," *Am. J. Phys.* **54**, 282 (1986).

19. Hecht and Zajac, op. cit., Chap. 8.

20. Falk et al., op. cit., p. 362 ff.

21. W.B. Sehneider, "A surprising optical property of Plexiglas rods," *Am. J. Phys.* **59**, 1086 (1991).

22. G.B Friedmann and H.S. Sandhu, "Phase changes on reflection from a metallic surface," *Am. J. Phys.* **56**, 270 (1988).

23. H.M. Lai, et al., "Mechanical analog of optical retarders," *Am. J. Phys.* **54**, 455 (1986).

24. Sutton, op. cit., see. L-134, p. 427; Hipschman, op. cit., Recipe No. 96.

25. P.R. Chagnon, "Animated Displays III...," *Phys. Teach.* **31**, 32 (1993).

26. Sutton, op. cit., sec. L-129, p.425; R. A. Hultsch, "A demonstration of optical activity," *Phys. Teach.* **20**, 476 (1982).

27. Polarizer Division, 1 Upland Road, Norwood, MA 02062; 800-225-2770.

28. C. Taylor, *The Art and Science of Lecture Demonstration* (Adam Hilger, Bristol, 1988, distributed by American Institute of Physics), p. 129.

29. G. Freier and B.G. Eaton, "Optical activity demonstrator," *Am. J. Phys.* **43**, 939 (1975).

30. Herbach and Rademan, 18 Canal Street, Bristol, PA 19007-0122; 215-788-5583.

31. B.G. Eaton and J.B. Johnston, "More about light scattering demonstrations," *Am. J. Phys.* **53**, 184 (1985); R. Hipschman, op. cit., Recipe No. 95.

32. Sutton, op. cit., sec. L-127, p. 424.

Chapter 5

Electrostatics

Animated Displays VI: Electrostatic Motors and Water Dropper

Paul Chagnon, Physics Department, University of Notre Dame, Notre Dame, IN 46556

This time, our display case[1] holds three uncommon electrostatic demonstrations: two types of electrostatic motor and a Kelvin water-dropper generator. These all run automatically and their action attracts the attention of passersby. All of this display is constructed from commonly available materials without any special shop facilities.

It must come as a disillusionment, if not a disappointment, for people first learning electricity to find out that "electric" motors in practice are actually magnetic. Indeed the common wisdom is that truly electric (i.e., "electrostatic") motors just do not exist. This tends to relegate the electrostatic force, in some minds, to the level of a scientific curiosity. In fact, electrostatic motors are merely less practical than electromagnetic ones, for reasons mainly to do with properties of materials. In the developing area of micromachinery, electrostatic motors may well come into their own.[2]

Professor Oleg Jefimenko of West Virginia University has specialized in the study of electrostatics. He classifies electrostatic motors as contact motors, spark motors, corona motors, and so on, according to the method of charge transfer.[3] We selected the corona motor as easiest to build and operate (other than the familiar pinwheel or electric fly), and particularly as a good match for the water dropper. Another type of motor, a large spark motor, adds visual appeal to the display. It also makes the most tangible use of the Coulomb force between discrete charged objects, giving it maximum heuristic value.

Corona Motor

This corona motor (Fig. 1) is a contemporary realization of a sketch drawn by

Phys. Teach. **34**, 491-494 (Nov. 1996)

Fig. 1. Corona-type electrostatic motor at rest. The pickle-jar rotor pivots on a pencil point; metal tabs are needed for static balance. One pair of corona needles or pins is seen here; the base readily accommodates a second pair. This motor is not truly electro*static*, of course. It operates on up to 100 nA at about 10 kV, for a power on the order of 1 mW. The work of gravity on the falling water in the adjacent Kelvin generator provides this power.

Jefimenko[3] from the verbal description of an "electric whirlwind" by Gruel in 1871.[4] Each set of needles, considered as one electrode, deposits charge by atmospheric conduction (corona) on the adjacent glass. This area of glass is repelled by the needles and their supporting rod, and attracted to the next electrode which is oppositely charged. There, an opposite corona current reverses the charge and rotation continues.

For our corona motor, a pickle jar of about 400 g mass and 11 cm in diameter serves as the rotor. We glued a small brass tubing plug, which happens to have a conical interior, into the bottom of the jar, then inverted it to pivot on the 0.5-mm tip of a mechanical pencil.

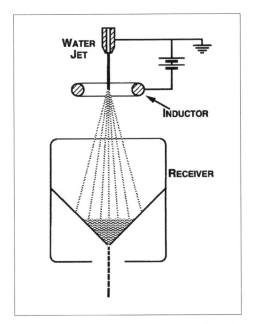

Fig. 2. Schematic cross section of a single Kelvin water dropper, adapted from Ref. 6. The water stream breaks up near the center of the inductor, resulting in individual charged drops. To the extent that they are not excessively repelled by one another and by the receiver, the drops fall into the receiver, carrying charge or current to it. Water drops with little charge drain from the hole in the cone or funnel inside the receiver. Two sets of such electrodes, cross-connected, form the self-acting generator. Some versions of water dropper omit the funnel; others use cylindrical inductors.

Each electrode consists of 12 short sewing pins, celled sequin pins, with their heads recessed into holes drilled in a 9-mm aluminum rod. Two or four of these rods, and the pencil pivot, are set into a base of Plexiglas™ or Lexan™, so that the points of the pins are about 2 mm from the glass. Adjustments do not appear to be critical, but of course the very low friction is essential.

The corona motor can start from rest because each row of needles is turned about 45° from the normal to the surface, so that the charge is not deposited directly under the body of each electrode. With one pair of electrodes, as in the figure, this motor is self-starting at about 14 kV and runs at some tens of rpm on a current of the order of 50 nA. Such currents can readily be produced with a Wimshurst machine, or extracted from a charged Leyden jar.

Originally with two pairs of electrodes (four sets of pins) our machine started and ran on as little as 9 kV. The rotational speed and the current are quite literally proportional; that is, if the rotor is prevented from turning, the current falls to zero, and as it picks up speed the current increases, apparently in a fixed ratio. This ratio is about the same whether one or two pairs of electrodes are in use. All this makes sense if the rotor is transporting charge from one electrode to the next with a constant surface density. In the actual display, the corona motor receives its power from the Kelvin water dropper, to be described.

When our corona motor reaches about 50 rpm, for want of dynamic balance it begins to wobble rather severely, so that the glass strikes against the corona pins. This does no apparent harm, but the resulting friction prevents any further increase in speed.

Kelvin Water Dropper

Under one name or another, this generator appears periodically in physics teachers' literature.[5] Anyone interested in the water dropper would be well advised to read Lord Kelvin's original paper.[6] Our version incorporates features from several of these articles. There is also a water dropper available commercially.[7]

In Fig. 2, a conducting ring (inductor) is mounted some distance beneath a small grounded nozzle, as near as possible to the height where the falling water stream breaks up into discrete droplets. If the inductor ring is biased negatively as shown, positive charge will be induced on the surface of the falling water, and each drop will carry away some positive charge. These drops give up their charge when they meet the funnel inside the receiver. The water re-forms into drops at the mouth of the funnel, but since this is located in the interior of a conductor there is little electric field and less charge is carried away than was brought in. No current is drawn from the inductor in the process.

Of course the same arrangement would work with the polarities reversed. Two sets of inductors and receivers thus can be cross-connected so that each inductor's potential is pro-

Fig. 3. The Kelvin water dropper, inside its shower curtain and inside the display case, connected to the corona motor. Assume, arbitrarily, that the black ring is negatively charged. That will induce a positive charge on the stream of water, which is a good conductor in this context. Where the stream breaks up into drops, each drop will retain some positive charge and carry it into the red (left side) bucket, making that positive. A wire connects the red bucket to the red ring (right side), which will then be positive and induce negative charge on its water stream, so that negative drops fall into the black bucket. This provides the negative charge on the black ring. When the pump seen at the bottom starts up, it takes 10 to 20 s for the voltage to build up until the corona motor starts turning. The latter then accelerates, usually up to about 50 rpm. Red and black distinguish the two polarities; on any given occasion either one may be positive and the other negative.

vided by the other receiver. This constitutes the complete water dropper (Fig. 3). In our case, the water streams are supplied by a small recirculating pump. Initially, there is bound to be some minuscule imbalance in the charges of the conductors. By positive feedback, the potentials build up exponentially, imperceptibly at first, but reaching tens of kilovolts in a time between 10 and 20 seconds.

Every article on water droppers points out, with good reason, that without some external load, the potentials increase until the repulsion of the droplets for one another and for the receiver causes the water to spray outward and miss the respective receiver. Some of the drops travel large distances horizontally and can even be seen arching upward in part of their flight. Other water from either stream collects on the oppositely charged inductor, wiring and insula-

tors, which eventually grounds out one of the inductors.

For a classroom demonstration, the spray is quite adequate evidence that the water dropper is working. For a display, it's desirable to have the water dropper supply energy to some load that shows it is producing electricity and simultaneously limits the potentials and the concomitant spraying. Others have used ringing bells and flashing discharge tubes. We sought something that would convey the impression of power more tangibly; hence the corona motor. Wedding the two is a matter of impedance matching, rendered tricky by the fact that the water dropper is a negative-resistance source, since its current production increases with increasing voltage. Fortunately, corona discharge tends to be a voltage-limiting effect. Earlier we mentioned reducing the corona motor from

Interactive Physics Demonstrations

Fig. 4. Spark-type electrostatic motor in the spirit of Benjamin Franklin. Dr. Franklin's motors were made of thimbles, glass rods, and hardwood spindles. Nowadays, pop cans and polystyrene foam are more abundant. In the outer ring (stator) the green and red cans are charged negative and positive respectively. When a can on the rotor passes a stator can, a spark jumps between them, giving the rotor can the same charge as the stator can. It is then repelled by that can and attracted to the next stator can, of opposite charge. This motor is not self-starting. It goes equally well in either direction, on about 20 kV and 1 to 5 μA from a power supply. The shaft In the center serves to suggest that useful power could be extracted from this motor.

two sets of electrodes to one. The reason for this now can be explained. With fewer electrodes, the voltage rises higher, which allows the water dropper to generate more current. The motor runs faster with more current, irrespective of the number of electrodes. The motor loading is still enough to limit the spraying of water to an acceptable rate.

Our water dropper's jets are assembled from plastic water pipe and brass tubing fittings, with orifices 2 to 3 mm in diameter. The inductors are plastic curtain-rod rings coated with colloidal graphite to make them conductive, and the receivers are aluminum kitchen canisters about 15 cm in diameter. Luckily, the canisters have edges rolled inward, as in Fig. 2. Both the inductors and the receivers are supported with plastic water pipe for insulation, and interconnected with high-voltage test lead wire. (Ignition wire would be as good.) The three plastic pipes are mounted on a ring stand

with ordinary laboratory clamps, making adjustment of positions very simple. The recirculating pump,[8] used previously in another display,[9] is similar to those sold in garden shops for small fountains.

Spark Motor

Probably the first electrostatic motors, i.e., those that transfer charge by sparks, originated with Benjamin Franklin in 1748. Jefimenko designed and built replicas of two of these, with authentic thimbles, glass rods, and hardwood spindles. I believe that the replicas were displayed at an AAPT meeting some decades ago. We turned to ubiquitous contemporary materials instead (Fig. 4). The bases for the rotor and stator are cut from expanded polystyrene, and all the electrodes are empty aluminum pop cans.[10] The principle is best seen with the aid of Fig. 5. The six green cans of the stator are connected (underneath) to the nega-

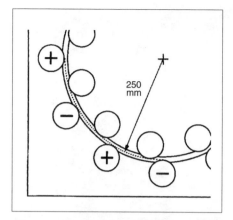

250 mm

Fig. 5. Partial plan of the spark motor. The stator (outer ring) and rotor consist of pop cans cemented to expanded polystyrene 4 cm thick. The rotor is bolted to a small phonograph turntable (sans motor, of course). The mean radius and spacings were chosen after some preliminary experiments with charged pop cans.

tive power supply terminal, alternating with the six red ones, which are positive. Each can on the rotor is insulated and acts independently. The clearance between the rotor and stator cans is about 2 mm. As a rotor can passes, say, a positive stator can, a spark jumps between them and the rotor can becomes positively charged, so it is repelled by that stator can and attracted to the next one. Upon reaching the next one, another spark passes and the sign of the rotor can reverses, so the process repeats.

Experiments conducted beforehand on pairs of pop cans indicated that, with these large conductors at short distances, the major force is actually the attraction between the induced dipoles in the cans, irrespective of polarity. Since this larger component is always attractive, its effect cancels on the whole as one can passes another; therefore, it is legitimate to explain our spark motor's operation in terms of the monopole forces. (This would not be a concern with Dr. Franklin's motors, whose proportions were quite different.) These experiments also guided us to design the motor so that the stator cans would be only 3 to 4 diameters apart.

A piece of thick plywood 0.7 m square, to fit the available space, serves as the platform for this motor. Raised on spacers cut from scraps of the expanded polystyrene, the stator ring is glued in place. (All fastening is with clear silicone caulk.) In the center we mounted the bearing from a small phonograph turntable. The rotor is attached to the turntable itself. We glued one stator can in place, then used it as a reference for all the rotor cans, gluing them in place with about 2 mm clearance. One rotor can then became the reference for the remaining stator cans. The phonograph turntable bearing turned out to have more play than anticipated, so the actual clearance between rotor and stator can vary from almost nothing to over 3 mm. At the actual operating voltage, sparks can jump such distances easily. Since the numbers of rotor (11) and stator (12) cans is incommensurate, no two sparks occur simultaneously; rather, there are 132 equally spaced small sparks to a revolution, giving our motor a continual soft crackling sound. (One of the Franklin replicas appears to have 23 rotor and two stator electrodes; the other has 6 and 6.)

It is evident that the spark motor can run in either rotational sense, but unfortunately it is not self-starting. It depends on inertia to keep going, and this in relation to the friction of the bearing sets a minimum speed. Our motor can run at about 10 rpm, on 1 μA average current at 18 kV. A small increase in voltage takes it to 50 rpm on 5 or 6 μA. It appears to be able to go quite a bit faster. Actually, we added resistors of 1 GΩ in each power-supply lead to stabilize the speed and make the motor safer to approach. This required raising the applied voltage to about 25 kV.

The power supply for the spark motor came from an old black-and-white television projector. A knowledgeable and cautious person could easily extract similar power from a disused color TV set; however, it was most convenient in developing both these motors to be able to control and measure the power applied.

Installation

A wooden box or tray about 8 cm deep, lined with polyethylene sheet, serves as the sump for the water dropper. The recirculating pump lies in the water at the bottom. We fashioned a ring stand out of brass shop scrap to stand in the center of this box; on it are assembled the pipes for the jets and those supporting the inductors and receivers. A clear plastic curtain that hangs from the ceiling of the display case and falls just inside the sump keeps water spray from reaching either electrostatic motor. Leads from the two receivers pass through holes in this curtain, to the corona motor. It is necessary to add distilled water at about two-week intervals to make up for evaporation.

The combination of water dropper and corona motor worked reliably in the open but failed after being enclosed in the display case, presumably due to the humidity. The display case is equipped with an exhaust fan but the air flow is nearly imperceptible. We found that shining a heat lamp, operating at very low power, on the corona motor cured that problem. The display, specifically the pump and some lights, is activated by a combination of a push button and a motion detector,[11] with the motion detector timer set at 1 minute. This keeps the water dropper from running unnecessarily, and so limits the amount of water that collects on the insulators. Of course enthusiastic watchers occasionally keep it running until the water dropper fails temporarily.

Since the spark motor is not self-starting, we simply let it run continually near the low end of its speed range. After a few months, there is no clear evidence that the sparking has a detrimental effect on the aluminum cans. The motor occasionally does stop; usually this correlates with increases in ambient humidity. We have considered installing a starter in the form of a small fan that would blow tangentially on the rotor.

Future Possibilities

Electrostatic motors can be addictive. It would be easy to construct a self-starting motor in the style of the spark motor described, but with a spark commutator separate from the attracting and repelling pop cans. Providing the spark motor with two good bearings would al-

low mechanical power to be taken off with a belt drive. Another possibility is an alternating-current version where the stator would produce a rotating field with the aid of R-C phase shifting circuits. Jefimenko[3] has constructed corona motors and electret motors in the fractional-horsepower range.

References

1. P.R. Chagnon, "Animated displays: Coupled mechanical oscillators," *Phys Teach.* **30**, 275 (1992).

2. M. Minsky, *Sci. Am.* **271**, 109 (October 1994); K. J. Gabrid, *Sci. Am.* **273**, 150 (September 1995).

3. O.D. Jefimenko, *Electrostatic Motors* (Electret Scientific Co., Star City, WV, 1973), p. 61.

4. *Poggendorffs Annalen der Physik und Chemie,* Ser. 2. **144** (1871), p. 644.

5. R.M. Sunon, *Demonstration Experiments in Physics* (McGraw-Hill, New York, 1938), p. 261; A.D. Moore, *Electrostatics* (Doubleday, New York, 1968), p. 175; H.F. Meiners, *Physics Demonstration Experiments* (Ronald, New York, 1970), pp. 847-849 and p. 1311-1312; M. Fast, "Electrostatic lobby display," *Phys. Teach.* **10**, 100 (1972); C. Bettis, "The Ting-a-Ling machine," *Phys. Teach.* **26**, 304 (1988).

6. William Thompson, Lord Kelvin, "On a self-acting apparatus for multiplying and maintaining electric charges...," in *Reprint of Papers on Electrostatics and Magnetism,* 2nd ed. (Macmillan, London, 1884), p. 323 [reprinted from *Proc. Roy. Soc.*, June 20, 1867].

7. Model ES-214 from Educational Equipment Co., Box 2102, Vernon, CT 06066.

8. Model P-AAA, Little Giant Pump Co., Oklahoma City, OK 73112.

9. P.R. Chagnon, "Animated displays V: Relaxation oscillators," *Phys. Teach.* **32**, 432 (1994).

10. W.F. Hosford and J.L. Duncan, "The aluminum beverage can," *Sci. Am.* **271**, 48 (September 1994).

11. P.R. Chagnon, "Animated displays II: Multiple reflections," *Phys. Teach.* **30**, 488 (1992).

Electrostatic Lobby Display

Menno Fast, Beblen Laboratory of Physics, University of Nebraska, Lincoln, NE 68508

The Kelvin electrostatic generator, so aptly described by Professor A.D. Moore,[1,2] when connected to a bell and chime arrangement such as Sargent-Welch No. 2039, becomes a new attraction and provokes interest even in the nonscience student (Fig. 1). We placed ours beside the Christmas tree allowing the spectators to recycle the water as it flowed from the top reservoir to the lower one. The pleasing tintannabulations of the bells, mixed with the blinking lights of the Christmas tree, served to renew the Christmas spirit in many a student and awakened a new interest in the science of electrostatics.

This apparatus was constructed from various sizes of tin cans. Tops and bottoms were removed from four cans in the central part of the apparatus; two of these have metal funnels inserted to catch the water droplets and conduct the charges to the outer surface of the cans (Fig. 2). The fact that the water is discharged from a neutral zone at the center of a can insures that the droplets will not carry away the charges as they leave the funnels.

Medicine droppers make excellent water jets and their flow can be controlled by pinch clamps connected to rubber tubing. If the bell arrangement is homemade, care must be taken

Fig. 1. Kelvin electrostatic generator made from tin cans. Water dripping from the top reservoir generates static charges that ring bells and spark student interest.

to mount it on an adequately insulated stand or suspend it by a silk thread. Bare aluminum is recommended for the leads from the oppositely charged cans to the bells. Aluminum allows itself to be coiled neatly yet supports its own weight thus eliminating the possibility of short circuits which usually plague dangling wires.

Sometimes the apparatus does not work instantly but one can easily detect when the apparatus is accumulating charges by the fact that the water droplets begin to fall in a spray rather than a stream, as droplets with like charges repel each other. In fact, the magnitude of the forces exerted by these charges is sufficient to deflect them considerably from their normal vertical path. Observations will be made as students reflect on the operation of this apparatus.

Many departments may already have a Kelvin water drop apparatus but perhaps have not thought about coupling it to the bell and chime system. We owe our apparatus to the efforts of Professor T. Jorgensen.

References

1.   A.D. Moore, *Electrostatics* (Doubleday, New York, 1968), pp. 17-177.

2.   Harry F. Meiners, *Physics Demonstration Experiments* (Ronald, New York, 1970), pp. 847-848.

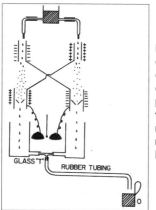

Fig. 2. Schematic of the Kelvin electrostatic generator showing placement of funnels and other modifications to make an effective lobby display.

Phys. Teach. **10**, 100-101 (Feb. 1972)

The "Ting-a-Ling" Machine

Clifford Bettis, Department of Physics and Astronomy, University of Nebraska-Lincoln, Lincoln, NE 68588-0111

The apparatus shown in Fig. 1 makes an intriguing hallway demonstration; it is an updated version of an apparatus described by Menno Fast.[1] When the pot on top is filled with water, and the water is allowed to flow through the two nozzles, an electrical potential difference builds up between the pans labeled 2A and 3A in both Figs. 2 and 3. These pans are connected in turn to the Franklin's bells apparatus mounted in front of the machine. After a short time the bells begin to ring. It has never failed to work even in extremely humid weather, and usually I have to fill it only once at the beginning of the day since interested bypassers continually refill the upper pot for me.

Design

In designing the device, I was aiming at a layout that would be as simple as possible so that its electrical connections could be easily seen. Therefore I decided to make all the parts that are conductors out of stainless steel and and of the parts that are insulators out of acrylic. An exploded line drawing of most of the components is shown in Fig. 2.

The pots were part of a couple of nested stainless steel cooking pot sets. The pots labeled 2A and 2B in Fig. 2 have their bottoms cut off so that they are cylinders; pots 3A and 3B have small tubes soldered into their bottoms so that water can drain away into the catch pots (1A and 1B). The valves used to control the water flow are aquarium values. The nozzles are glass and were drawn out for me by a glass blower, though eyedropper nozzles would work as well. The bells are an older version of a commercially available apparatus (Sargent-Welch 2039). The tripod base was taken from an old Young's modulus apparatus. Detail drawings of the individual parts are available from me.

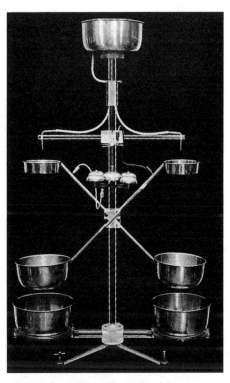

Fig. 1. The "ting-a-ling" machine.

Operation

The apparatus works as follows. Suppose cylinder 2A (Fig. 3) has a slightly positive charge. Then negative charge in the stream of water dropping from above will be attracted to it. (As I will explain later, even fairly pure water is a good conductor for this device.) As the water stream breaks into drops (the flow is adjusted with the aquarium valves so that the stream breaks into drops at about the middle of cylinder 2A or 2B), the drops carry a negative charge. When these drops strike pot 3A, they give up most of their charge to it and some of this charge is conducted by the steel connecting crosspiece to cylinder 2B. Now cylinder 2B has a negative charge and draws down positive

Phys. Teach. **26**, 304-306 (May 1988)

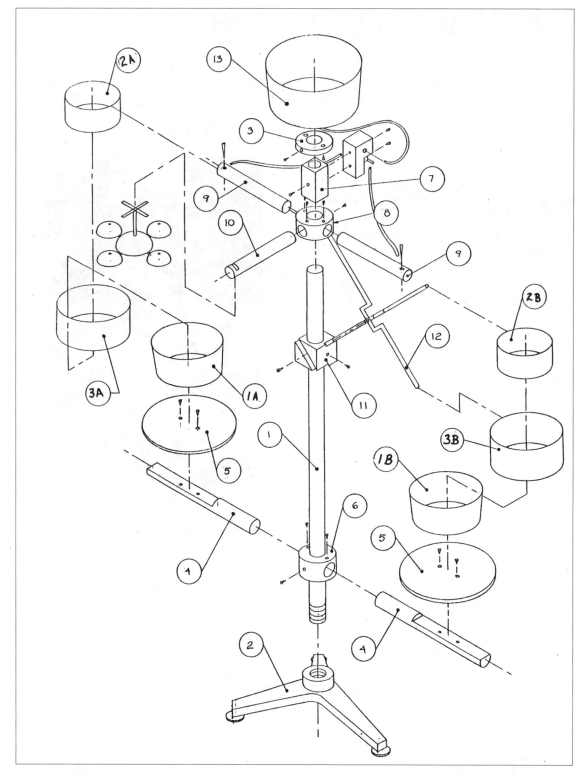

Fig. 2. Exploded line drawing of the "ting-a-ling" machine: (1) center rod; (2) stand; (3) container support; (1A, 1B) "catch" pots; (2A, 2B) stainless steel cylinders; (3A, 3B) stainless steel pots; (4) supporting arm; (5) disk; (6) collar; (7) valve supporter; (8) nozzle arm collar; (9) nozzle arm; (10) bell arm; (11) conductor support; (12) conducting rod; (13) container.

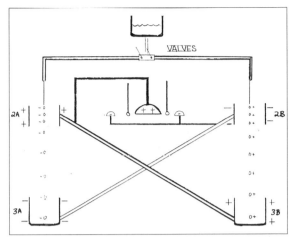

Fig. 3. Schematic drawing of the "ting-a-ling" machine.

charge in the water stream. This charge is deposited in pot 3B which is connected to cylinder 2A by the other steel connecting crosspiece, thus increasing the positive charge already there.

In this way a potential difference is built up between cylinder 2A and cylinder 2B. These cylinders then are connected to the Franklin's bells apparatus in which the potential difference between the inner and outer gongs creates a non-uniform electric field between the gongs. This field does two things: It induces a dipole moment in the clappers and, because it is a non-uniform field, it exerts a net force on

them. The clappers then move and strike either the inner or outer gong, pick up the same sign charge as that gong and are then repelled to strike the oppositely charged gong. The process repeats as long as the field is maintained.

Where does the original charge come from? Perhaps a passing cosmic ray or (more likely) just the stray electric fields in the environment create small potential differences that are responsible for the initial seed charge.

Remarks

Finally, further information about the conductivity of the water is appropriate. Consider the vessel of water at the top as an RC circuit with the capacitance being provided by the pot of water and the resistance being the resistance of the stream of water from the pot to the point where it breaks into drops. Approximate the pot by considering it to be a conducting sphere about 20 cm in diameter. Its capacitance then is about 10 pF. The length of time it takes for a "parcel" of water to leave the pot and flow to the point where it breaks into drops is about one second. Therefore, as long as the resistance of the water stream is less than about $10^{11}\Omega$, water can be considered a conductor in this application.

References

1. *Phys. Teach.* **10**, 100 (1972).

Chapter 6

Chaos

A Simple Hallway Demonstration of Chaos

Seamus Lagan, Department of Physics, Whittier College, Whittier, CA 90608

In the hallway of the Science Building we have a display case for which I am constantly seeking interesting items. This hallway is a well-traveled thoroughfare and for security reasons the display case is kept locked, limiting the amount of interaction with the demonstrations. Under these circumstances it is difficult to come up with simple demonstrations that are not either static or periodic. Such displays tend to lose their appeal after a time and are ignored by passersby. An ideal demonstration is one that changes over time in a nonperiodic fashion and also involves a relatively current physics topic. Chaotic systems obviously fit the bill.

One such system is a compass needle in an oscillating magnetic field. The setup described by Meissner and Schmidt[1] is more sophisticated than is necessary for a hallway demonstration, but a variation of it is very simple to put together and has the added visual impact of involving rotation about two axes rather than one. The demonstration consists simply of a signal generator, a solenoid, and a magnaprobe. The magnaprobe is a small bar magnet mounted so that it is free to rotate about two mutually perpendicular axes. Generally it is used to find the direction of magnetic field lines. It is commercially available at very low cost.[2]

Place the magnaprobe at one end of the solenoid with the rotation axes at some arbitrary angle to the axis of the solenoid. (I have one of the magnaprobe axes horizontal, and therefore I have the solenoid axis tipped at an angle to the horizontal.) Then apply to the solenoid an alternating signal of sufficient strength to produce a magnetic field capable of affecting the magnaprobe. By playing around with the signal strength, signal frequency, and magnaprobe orientation you should soon find a chaotic regime in which the magnaprobe rotates about both axes in an apparently random fashion. Frequencies that work well on my system are between 1 and 2 Hz.

I did have some trouble at the start finding a chaotic regime. The magnaprobe tended to get stuck in one position after a while, and increasing the signal strength only put it into a periodic regime. Finally I realized that I had the solenoid aligned (quite by accident) approximately along the direction of the Earth's magnetic field. I moved the solenoid so that its axis was perpendicular to the Earth's field, and this cured the problem.

This demonstration is very easily put together from equipment found in any physics department. It illustrates the production of magnetic fields by currents, the effect of a magnetic field on a dipole, and the phenomenon of deterministic unpredictability (chaos).

References

1. H. Meissner and G. Schmidt, *Am. J. Phys.* **54**, 800 (1985).

2. Frey Scientific, Catalog #15281.

Phys. Teach. **29**, 461 (Oct. 1991)

The Perplexing Pendulum

Joe Pizzo, Department of Physics, Lamar University,
Beaumont, TX 77710

This exhibit is a scaled-up version of a toy I once had. It is essentially a spherical pendulum with a ceramic ring magnet in place of a bob. The pendulum is suspended over a table into which several more ceramic ring magnets have been hidden (see Fig. 1). An intricate magnetic field pattern "competes" with the gravitational field. The resulting forces along the pendulum's path cause a wild, jerky, seemingly capricious motion, which has to be seen to be appreciated.

The assembly of such a pendulum can be done in many different ways. The description given here is of one that has successfully withstood the manipulation and abuse of numerous participants for three years, with no need for the replacement of any parts.

A rubber stopper is fitted tightly into a ceramic ring magnet and attached by a long screw to one end of a wooden dowel, which serves as the rod for the pendulum. An eyescrew is fastened into the other end of the dowel. The support for the pendulum consists of a horizontal rod, to which a meter stick clamp is attached. The bolt which is designed to secure a meter stick is replaced with an eyebolt. The "eye" is opened enough to slip into the "eye" on the end of the rod and clamped shut again. When the rod is suspended, as shown in Fig. 1, it will be free to swing in all directions.

A card table with a badly torn surface was rescued from a trash pile for this exhibit. Six ceramic ring magnets, all with their poles repelling the magnetic bob, were placed symmetrically in the center of the table. (Other arrangements, with differing polarities, also prove interesting.) Padding was removed, where necessary, to form a partial recess for the magnets. A thin sheet of masonite was cut with the same dimensions as the table surface and placed over the magnets. The masonite was se-

Fig. 1. A spherical pendulum, with a magnetic bob, displays capricious behavior when suspended over an array of magnets hidden in the surface of the table.

cured to the table with duct tape around all edges. In addition to providing security for the magnets, this type of subterfuge adds an element of intrigue, since the graphics for the exhibit simply state, "Set the pendulum in motion." This truly gives the participant the chance for discovery.

If it is desired to have the magnets exposed, a Plexiglas cover could be installed over the table surface, at a distance slightly greater than the thickness of a magnet. "Finger holes" in the Plexiglas would allow the participant to alter the array of magnets, adding an extra dimension of interaction to the exhibit.

Phys. Teach. **24**, 360 (Sept. 1986)

Interactive Physics Demonstrations

Chaos in the Corridor

Alan Cromer, Department of Physics, Northeastern University, Boston, MA 02115;
Christos Zahopoulos *and* **Michael B. Silevitch,** Center for Electromagnetics
Research, Northeastern University, Boston, MA 02155

The principal lesson we learn from the study of chaos is that deterministic systems are not necessarily predictable. This, as Max Dresden put it, is "a major scientific reorientation" and as such "will sooner or later exert a major influence on the teaching program."[1]

One of the simplest and most dramatic demonstrations of chaos is the double pendulum. If rigidly constructed, it makes a durable corridor exhibit that never ceases to fascinate and delight all who see it. Double-pendulum exhibits — and other exhibits that we are developing[2] — are being placed in middle schools in the Boston area as part of a larger project to improve science education. In an informal and spontaneous way, these exhibits give every passerby the opportunity to experience the joy and wonder of science. We see students interacting with the pendulum exhibit throughout the day and after school as well. Of course the theory of chaos is beyond middle school children, but the exhibit gives them something to wonder and think about.

The Double Pendulum

A simple double pendulum consists of two masses m_1 and m_2 connected by two massless rods of length L_1 and L_2, as shown in Fig. 1a. Each rod is free to swing through a complete circle in a fixed plane. The system, which has two degrees of freedom, is described by the two angles θ_1 and θ_2.

In practice, it is hard to find rigid massless rods, so we built the system shown in Fig. 1b. It consists of an upper arm of length L_1 = 23 cm made of two aluminum bars affixed at the upper end on bearings to a rigidly mounted rod, and a lower arm of length L_2 = 20 cm made of a single aluminum bar that rotates on a bearing between the two bars of the upper arm.

The double pendulum is commonly used as an example in Lagrangian mechanics and the theory of small oscillations.[3,4] The Lagrangian of the system yields two coupled nonlinear second-order differential equations in the vari-

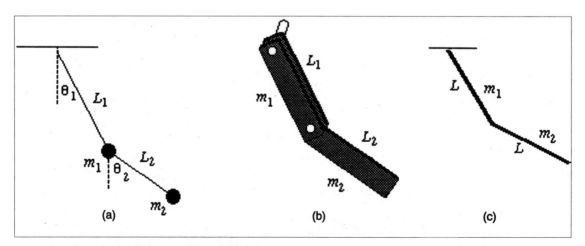

Fig. 1. (a) Simple double pendulum; (b) physical double pendulum used in the corridor exhibits; (c) model double pendulum consisting of two uniform rods of equal lengths and unequal masses.

Phys. Teach. **30**, 382-383 (Sept. 1992)

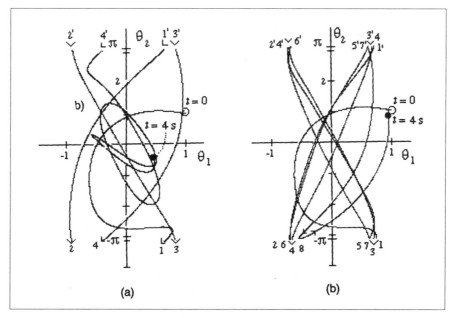

Fig. 2. Numerical plots of θ_2 vs θ_1 for the model double pendulum in Fig. 1(c). These are both 4-s trajectories starting from rest with nearly the same initial positions. The numbers show points where the lower arm passes through $\theta_2 = \pm \pi$. (a) Initial position $\theta_1 = \theta_2 = 1.0$ rad; (b) Initial position $\theta_1 = 1.01$ rad and $\theta_2 = 1.0$ rad. Note that at position 8 the lower arm does not reach $-\pi$, and so does not make a complete rotation.

ables θ_1 and θ_2.[4,5] For small angles (θ_1 and θ_2 << 1 rad), these equations become linear, with solutions that are linear combinations of two harmonic oscillations with different periods. In one of these oscillations, or normal modes, the upper and lower arms oscillate in opposite directions. In the other mode, the arms oscillate in the same direction. For our double pendulums, the periods of these two modes are 0.58 and 1.0 s, respectively.

The effects of nonlinearity become pronounced as the angles are increased. If the upper arm is released from an angle greater than 90°, the subsequent motion is chaotic. The system now has enough energy for the lower arm to rotate in complete circles. These rotations go clockwise and counterclockwise in apparently random alterations. With good bearings and rigid support, this chaotic motion persists for 30 s or more. During this time, the lower arm seems to have a mind of its own as it spins for a while one way and then another.

Our pendulums are mounted in a rigid aluminum frame with gussets on either side to prevent lateral vibration. The frame is bolted to a plywood display case about 1 m high. The double pendulum on display in the lobby of the Dana Research Building at Northeastern University is completely open, while the one at the Museum of Science is completely enclosed in a Plexiglas™ case. An extension rod through the bearing on the lower arm passes through a semicircular slot in the Plexiglas. Visitors release the upper arm from various angles by moving the rod along the slot.

This limits the interaction of the public with the display in the interest of safety. Pendulums placed in public schools have an open Plexiglas frame that allows complete access to the pendulum while discouraging heads and fingers from getting too close. Hopefully, this is a reasonable compromise between safety and accessibility. (Detailed shop drawings are available on request.)

Theory

Chaotic motion is motion in which any arbitrarily small change in the initial conditions results in a large change in the subsequent motion. This is worse than it sounds. It means that any "noise" in the initial values of the positions and velocities of a system will be greatly amplified with time. Since any numerical calculation introduces noise at each step, every calculation is in principle arbitrary and random. Numerical calculations are nevertheless of value, because their arbitrary and random results are believed to be representative of the real motion.

For mathematical simplicity, we consider a model double pendulum consisting of two uniform rods of equal length L and masses m_1 and m_2 (Fig. 1c). With $L = 20$ cm, and $m_2/m_1 = 0.5$, this model corresponds roughly to our real double pendulum. The periods of the normal modes of the model are 0.44 and 1.0 s (compared with 0.58 and 1.0 s of the real double pendulum).

Figure 2 is a plot of θ_2 vs θ_1 for 4 s, obtained from numerical integration of the model system. Figure 2a is for the system starting at rest at $\theta_1 = \theta_2 = 1.0$ rad and Fig. 2b is for the system starting at rest at $\theta_1 = 1.01$ rad and $\theta_2 = 1.0$ rad. Even during the first 4 s, the two motions — with nearly identical initial conditions — are very different. In Fig. 2a, the lower arm makes four complete revolutions, whereas in Fig. 2b it makes seven. The real system exhibits similar variability in its motions. It is this extreme sensitivity to initial conditions that characterizes chaotic motion.

Conclusions

The physical double pendulum provides an introduction to chaotic motion that is appropriate for all age levels. The novelty of the motion is both entertaining and instructive. The device is easily made, the main requirements being good bearings and a rigid frame with supporting gussets.

Acknowledgment

Our double pendulums have been built with great beauty and precision by Richard Ahlquist and Stephen DiCiaccio. David Burke prepared the shop drawings.

References

1. M. Dresden, *Phys. Teach.* **30**, 74 (1992).
2. We have been building double-pendulum chaos exhibits since 1989, with funding from the Museum of Science (Boston), Northeastern University, and the National Science Foundation.
3. H. Goldstein, *Classical Mechanics,* 2nd ed. (Addison-Wesley, Reading, MA, 1980).
4. D. Hestenes, *New Foundations for Classical Mechanics* (Kluwer Academic Pub., Norwell, MA, 1986).
5. T. Shinbrot et al., *Am. J. Phys.* **60**, 491 (1992).

Multiple Exhibit Displays & Mini-Museums

Interactive Hallway Physics for Elementary Schools

K. David Pinkerton, Smoky Hill High School, 16100 E. Smoky Hill Road, Aurora, CO 80015

There is no paucity of novel teaching methods in physics. Inspiration to act and follow through on ideas is more scarce, however. I have read the "Deck the Halls" section of *The Physics Teacher* for years; I've visited the Exploratorium Museum in San Francisco during AAPT meetings; finally I decided that I too could produce physics exhibits!

A recent issue of *TPT* featured an interactive display facility permanently installed outside a first-year physics lecture room in a university.[1] I describe here the construction and general use of a portable, freestanding exhibit space that can be placed in public schools.

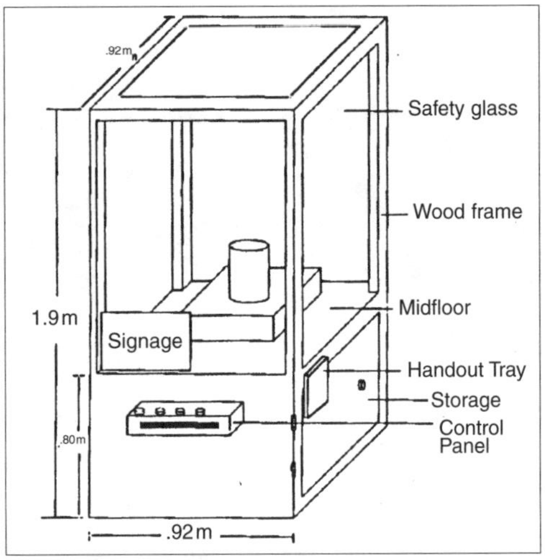

Considerations

The safety, hallway management, and durability factors associated with placing interactive physics demonstrations in public schools are unique. As a high-school physics instructor, I had designed, installed, and maintained several such demonstration units at Smoky Hill High School. This effort gave me the experience needed to develop a freestanding, portable, secure, and interactive set of exhibits-based physics demonstrations for lower grades in public schools.

The "package" currently operational in four elementary schools and one middle school in our district consists of:

* Display cabinet with control panel and handout tray.
* Nine interactive demonstrations (one new exhibit per month).
* Teacher's guide with instructions, photos, schematic diagrams, parts lists, and vendors.
* "Signage" for each demonstration.
* Supplemental "do-at-home" experiments for the handout tray.

Phys. Teach. **29**, 166-168 (March 1991)

Fig. 1. Schematic of cabinet.

Fig. 2. Freestanding demonstration cabinet on site.

I conduct a training workshop for on-site teachers so they will be comfortable and familiar with the display. These teachers are responsible for changing and maintaining the demonstrations. Each year we meet to construct at least one more demonstration. This insures that the operation will continue to develop and gives a sense of ownership of the project to the teachers at the schools.

A few principles guided the design of the cabinet and demonstrations. Great effort was expended to keep the costs down while maintaining a high-quality, professional appearance. I used commonplace or household parts whenever possible to convey to users that doing physics involves "normal" things. Each item should be of low-maintenance design yet reproducibly perform its tasks. The emphasis is on investigation and curiosity, not on conveying facts.

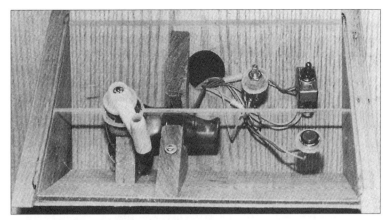

Fig. 3. Control panel interior is visible.

Fig. 4. Details of timer, which sits on the midfloor.

Construction

The cabinet was designed to give a stable and highly visible venue for each demonstration. A diagram (Fig. 1) shows basic construction. Each wall has the same dimensions and is assembled in one piece. The edges are beveled and individual walls glued together. The door side is slightly smaller in order to accommodate a long section of piano hinge. Exact dimensions are not crucial, but the cabinet should easily fit through a classroom door. The midfloor is at a height for good viewing by the average fourth grader. A subfloor provides the storage platform. The large safety-glass windows allow for good viewing and the panel with door opens for easy access to the display and storage areas. A 120-V ac plug is mounted to the storage area floor with a retractable ex-

tension cord wired to it. Two holes are drilled into the midfloor for access to the power for any electrically controlled device. The cabinet utilized in one elementary-school media center is shown in Fig. 2.

The control panel (Fig. 3) is designed for visibility and flexibility. A 0.6-cm Plexiglas sheet with appropriate holes serves as the cover. It is easily changed and allows the user to see inside the control panel. The current model has one doorbell switch, one DPDT toggle, one 100-Ω trim pot, and one Genecon hand-held dc generator[2] mounted with only the business end of the control device accessible to students. All electrical connections are fed through a hole in the wall into the storage area.

The handout tray, mounted on the door, holds several copies of the appropriate "do-at-home" experiments. Ideally, a user will interact with the demonstration and desire to do more. The signage refers to the handouts and encourages students to continue the investigations at home by performing the experiments mentioned with household objects. This is an excellent outlet for the activities mentioned in the "String and Sticky Tape" section of *The Physics Teacher*.

An important control feature of this package is the timer. I used a National Controls Corporation T2K-00300-461 single-shot timer. It allows for 120-V ac on cycle for an uninterruptable time of up to 3 min. The timer is used to turn on dc power supplies and to operate 120-V ac devices. It is activated by pushing the doorbell switch on the control panel. Once activated, a timed sequence will transpire regardless of further attempts to initiate another sequence. I constructed a stand and mounting bracket out of Plexiglas to show as much of the "workings" of the timer as possible (Fig. 4).

The teacher's guide is available at cost from the author. It includes instructions, parts lists, vendors, signage, and at-home experiments for the handout tray. The teacher's guide text is stored on disk in Microsoft Word 2.0, and the signage/handouts are stored on disk in Page-maker, both Macintosh-compatible, if the reader prefers that format.

"Hallway Physics" has proven to be rewarding for both teachers and students. Students enjoy a nonthreatening environment in which

to experience true individualized instruction. They can operate these demonstrations as often as needed for their own understanding. They experience the reality that "physics happens" even though a teacher is not holding or operating the device. As a result, physics is demystified and young students develop confidence when interacting with devices. Teachers model a "hands-on" approach to science by actively maintaining and changing the demonstrations. They grow in physics knowledge, creatively adapt the program to their students' needs, and also gain basic manipulative skills and problem-solving expertise.

Standing at a distance from one of the cabinets and observing students interacting with the current display yields its own rewards for the designer too! I have seen users with mouth unknowingly agape literally press their noses against the glass to get a closer look at the action. Peers frequently are called over to the display to "check it out." Wonderful unstructured interactions among students are accompanied by vigorous hand movements and engaging dialog. The wide-eyed scrutiny of such demonstrations obviously stimulates even the young student's curiosity and acceptance of physics.

References

1. John Campbell, "Canterbury's physics display facility," *Phys. Teach.* 27, 526 (1989).

2. Catalog Part #S43917, Fisher-EMD, 4901 W LeMoyne St., Chicago, IL 60651, $27.

Laser Light Fantastic Lissajous Figures

K. David Pinkerton, Smoky Hill High School, 16100 E. Smoky Hill Road, Aurora, CO 80015

This demonstration is one of many that can be placed in a portable exhibition cabinet like the one just described.[1] These cabinets are located in elementary schools in our district; demonstrations are changed by on-site teachers each month.

The Laser Light Fantastic

Lasers produce a very narrow beam of almost monochromatic light. This beam of light remains collimated over distances of many meters. Reflecting the beam off a single rotating concave mirror produces an oval pattern on a screen. What happens when this oval shape reflects off a second concave mirror onto a screen? We see a design that is the result of interaction of two ovals. That is, when the rotational speeds of the mirrors are exactly matched, the ovals stand still on the screen. If one mirror spins faster than the other, the figures seem to spin. When the rotational speeds are in a whole-number ratio, the pattern again appears stationary. The difference will be in the number of lobes in the light display.

Construction

This demonstration requires a laser,[2] two concave mirrors mounted on 12-V dc motors, and the necessary power supplies and connections to produce the "lissajous" figures mentioned above. A schematic is shown in Fig. 1, a top-view photograph in Fig. 2, and a student interacting with the device is shown in Fig. 3. Ring stands and utility clamps are used to hold the motors/mirrors in an approximate "z" pattern from the laser to the screen. The exact position of the mirrors depends on the position of the beam from the laser. The first mirror should be slightly lower than the second one. A piece of paper can be

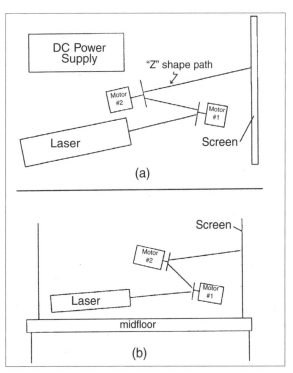

Fig. 1. Diagram for exhibition cabinet: (a) top view and (b) side view.

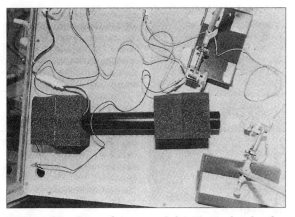

Fig. 2. Top view of "Laser Light Fantastic" in the cabinet.

used to locate the beam when aligning the laser, mirror #1, mirror #2, and screen. Once the laser beam shines on the desired position on the

Phys. Teach. **29**, 168-169 (March 1991)

screen, the necessary electrical connections should be made. An electrical connections diagram is shown in Fig. 4.

Adjust motor #1 speed with the variable dc power supply until a focused oval is produced on the screen. Supply power to motor #2 and turn the trim pot until a stationary figure results. Adjust the speed of motor #1 in order to produce the simplest figure in the mid range of the trim pot's movement. Make final adjustments to the beam and mirror alignment to produce a clear pattern. Tape down the ring stands because students will jar the cabinet occasionally. Darken the surrounding area somewhat if possible.

Helpful Hints

There are a few other tips that help this demonstration operate well. Use front-surfaced mirrors if possible. Most scientific supply companies have these. Keep them as clean as possible. I found the motors at a used electronics store, along with small plastic fans that fit exactly on their shafts. I attached the mirrors to the fans with silicone caulking. The variable resistor must be matched to the specific motor you buy. You must measure the resistance of the motor under the actual load. For our project, this was equivalent to a 100-Ω, one-turn trim pot. The dc power supply should be rated at 3 A and 12 V dc. The power supply should be plugged into the timer. You can use two separate power supplies or one that combines these features. They should both be of variable voltage. I scavenged my screen from a discarded projector screen, but any white surface will do. The screen hangs from an adjustable tension rod purchased from a local department store.

References

1. K. David Pinkerton, "Interactive hallway physics for elementary schools," *Phys. Teach.* **29**, 166 (1991).

2. Meredith Instruments, P.O. Box 1724, Glendale, AZ 85301. 5.0 mW HeNe laser 3SOH power supply.

Fig. 3. Student interacting with the demonstration.

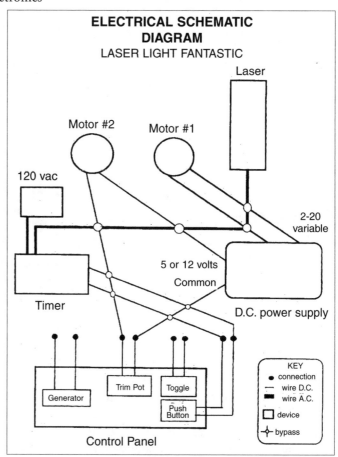

Fig. 4. Electrical connections diagram.

Sound Principles

K. David Pinkerton, Smoky Hill High School, 16100 E. Smoky Hill Road, Aurora, CO 80015

Here is a school hallway demonstration I guarantee to be a hit! I say that with confidence because of our experience[1] and because of the different levels at which users can approach the exhibit. Very young elementary-school children tend to playfully notice that the sounds produced somehow cause the oscilloscope to change; high school students observe the wavelength relationship between the notes.

Operation

The salient equipment consists of an electronic keyboard, oscilloscope, and the necessary connections to electrical power, all housed

Fig. 1. Elementary-school student interacting with "Sound Principles."

in a portable display cabinet, plus some burglar alarm pressure strips. Students turn on a timed sequence that allows them to step on one or more of eight pressure strips on the floor outside the cabinet. These "notes" are wired to an eight-note octave in the electronic keyboard. Two extra wires from the keyboard speaker are attached to the oscilloscope. The speaker remains "live" for students to hear the sounds while watching the characteristic wave forms on the oscilloscope screen. Figure 1 shows a young student interacting with the device as she steps on the pressure-pad keyboard on the floor.

Students readily see that sound can be represented by wavelike forms on the oscilloscope screen. If the teacher marks a set of crosshairs on the screen, users can observe that there is twice as much distance between two wave crests in low C as in high C. Stepping on two notes at once illustrates the waveforms associated with "pleasing" sounds vs dissonant chords. (A microphone could be placed in the control panel to inspire users to attempt to reproduce the keyboard notes with their voices.)

Construction

The electronic keyboard[2] is an important feature of this exhibit. I gained access to the notes through the back panel and traced the circuit from the desired keys to their metal terminals. I then soldered a single 10-cm, 20-gauge insulated wire to each desired note or terminal. (Touching two wires together has the same effect as pressing a certain key on the keyboard.) Trial and error rapidly enabled me to correctly pair wires and label the eight-note octave. With ribbon cable I attached (in one-note pairs) the wires protruding from the back of the keyboard to the external floor switches.

Phys. Teach. **30**, 446-447 (Oct. 1992)

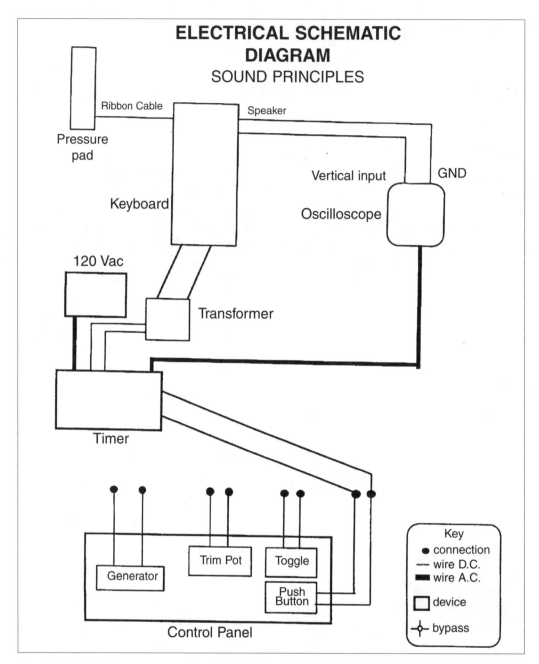

Fig. 2. Electrical diagram.

These external floor switches, which now replace the keys, are burglar alarm pressure strips frequently found under entryway doormats in stores. I used one strip per note. At the local hardware store I purchased a section of clear plastic stairway carpet protector and secured the eight pressure strips to it with duct tape. This assembled pressure pad measures approximately 1.5 by 1.0 m. I soldered two lengths of 20-gauge insulated wire strips to the keyboard speaker inputs and attached them to the oscilloscope input. Figure 2 gives the electrical schematic of the entire operation.

With your "foot notes" assembled, plug the transformer (which powers the keyboard) and the oscilloscope into the timer.[3] Set the keyboard on "flute" to produce a sinelike wave. Plug the timer into a wall outlet and attach the initiating switch to the "start" button on the control panel. Mount the appropriate explana-

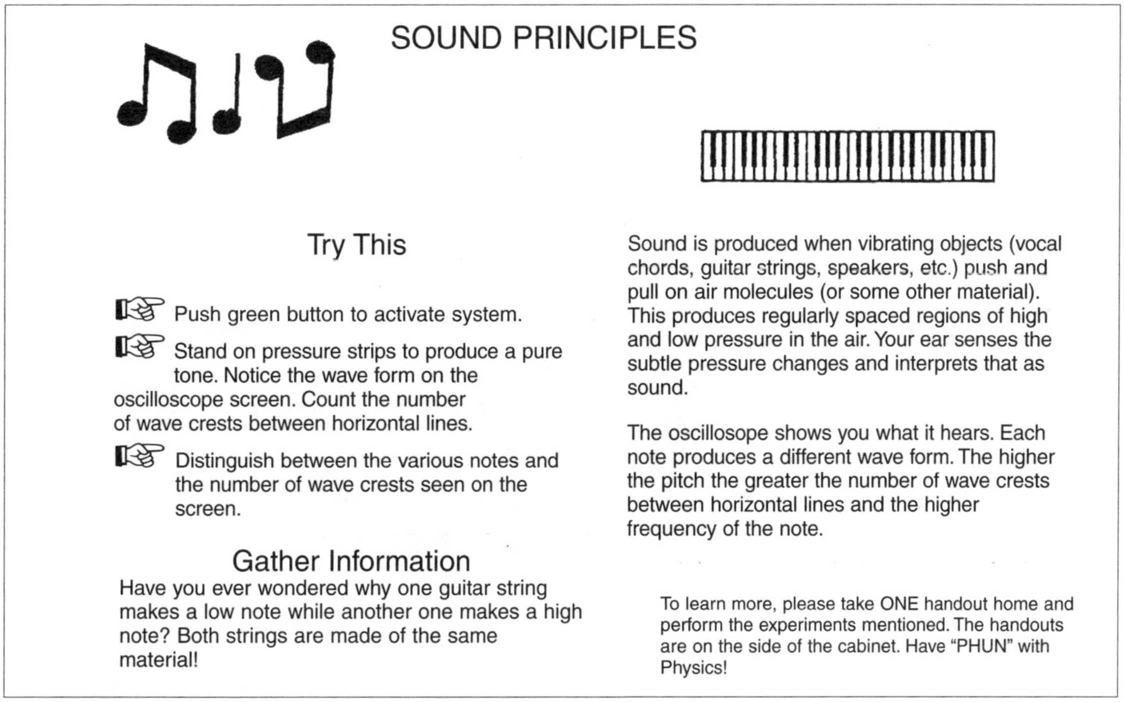

SOUND PRINCIPLES

Try This

☞ Push green button to activate system.

☞ Stand on pressure strips to produce a pure tone. Notice the wave form on the oscilloscope screen. Count the number of wave crests between horizontal lines.

☞ Distinguish between the various notes and the number of wave crests seen on the screen.

Gather Information

Have you ever wondered why one guitar string makes a low note while another one makes a high note? Both strings are made of the same material!

Sound is produced when vibrating objects (vocal chords, guitar strings, speakers, etc.) push and pull on air molecules (or some other material). This produces regularly spaced regions of high and low pressure in the air. Your ear senses the subtle pressure changes and interprets that as sound.

The oscillosope shows you what it hears. Each note produces a different wave form. The higher the pitch the greater the number of wave crests between horizontal lines and the higher frequency of the note.

To learn more, please take ONE handout home and perform the experiments mentioned. The handouts are on the side of the cabinet. Have "PHUN" with Physics!

Fig. 3. Explanation sign.

tion sign (Fig. 3) in the cabinet and fill the handout tray with appropriate "do-at-home" supplemental experiments. Step back and enjoy watching people having fun while learning.

References

1. The exhibit is one of nine demonstrations we've placed in several elementary schools in our district. Refer to K.D. Pinkerton, "Interactive hallway physics for elementary schools," *Phys. Teach.* **29,** 166 (1991) for more details on building and using freestanding exhibits such as the one discussed here.

2. Casio model PT-100.

3. Our oscilloscope came from a state surplus agency, and a 7.5-V dc transformer from the local Salvation Army store.

The Neon Sign

Samuel M. Sampere, Laboratory Manager, Department of Physics, Syracuse University, Syracuse, NY 13244-1130

What are a crumpled 55-gallon steel barrel and a tavern-style neon sign doing in the hallway of the physics building at a renowned and revered educational institution? It's attracting attention, stopping people in their tracks, and sending a message: physics is about size and color, motion and interaction; it's fun and it's interesting, something to experience for yourself.

As shown in Fig. 1, the highlight of our 17-ft display case is a large (3 x 3.5-ft) handcrafted neon sign. It's appealing, brightly lit, and located in the hallway near the building's entrance. Because this hallway is actually a thoroughfare connecting two very busy parts of campus, thousands of people walk by every day. Whenever I go past the display case between classes, someone will be playing with (or pondering over) the items behind the glass.

In the case with the neon sign is an incandescent light bulb and a fluorescent tube, both lit. Hanging next to the case is a hand-held spectroscope constructed for years of public abuse. It's made from PVC tubing painted flat black inside and out, with black Plexiglas ends on the tube. One end has a slit to allow light to enter; the other has a holographic diffraction grating.

From instructions posted beside the sign,

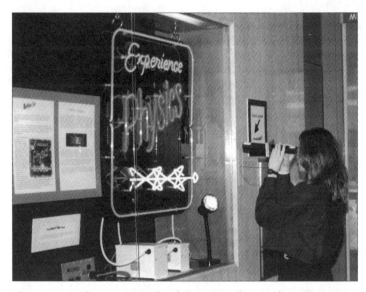

Fig. 1. Passerby gets involved in neon sign and spectroscope display.

Fig. 2. Corridor display features interactive instruction, physical phenomena apparatus, and public relations boards.

curious visitors first learn that the spectroscope separates light into all the colors that make up

Phys. Teach. **37**, 140-141 (March 1999)

that light. They're told how to use the spectro-scope, which end to look through, and how to align the instrument. First they look at the incandescent bulb and see that familiar rainbow (a continuous spectrum). Then they're led to point the tube at the orange letters of *Physics*, where they find colored vertical stripes in reds, oranges, and yellows — emission lines from neon gas. Then they aim the spectroscope toward the blue light of the word *Experience* and compare the spectra with those from the orange letters. Spectra from excited gases are not continuous and every gas has its own line spectrum. The orange tube contains neon (Ne) gas; and the blue tubes contain mercury (Hg) gas. Now the visitor is invited to aim the spectroscope at the fluorescent tubes at the top of the case and make comparisons between the Hg-filled tubes of the neon sign, the incandescent lamp, and the fluorescent lights. Our hallway investigators are learning things that scientists have understood for less than 100 years. Why learn about this? It's how fluorescent lights work. Astronomers use information like this to determine the composition of stars; geologists determine the composition of rocks using similar techniques. Pick up the spectroscope and you're hooked!

The bottom-most light of the neon sign is a three-dimensional model of an electromagnetic wave. The purple and yellow tubes represent the electric and magnetic fields, respectively. The white tube represents the Poynting vector. Light is, after all, an electromagnetic wave. Electromagnetic waves called microwaves heat our food. Electromagnetic waves called x-rays are used to take pictures of our skeletons. Electromagnetic waves called radio waves transmit audio and visual information to our radios and television sets.

Of course the neon sign is only part of the display (see Fig. 2). Next to it (moving right to left) is a tandem-double pendulum (two double pendula mounted on the same axle, but free to move independently of each other). At small starting amplitudes, the two pendula move in identical patterns for many oscillations. When the starting amplitudes are large, after two or three oscillations the motions of each are completely different. This demo has enormous play value; people love to watch the two swinging pendula.

The left-most two panels contain a map of the world. Surrounding the map are pictures of faculty and conference posters. If a physics faculty member is listed on a conference poster as either an organizer or invited speaker, that person's picture will be mounted in the display. A string connects the person to the location of the conference. Thus students and passersby see that our physics faculty are recognized around the world.

An interesting sidelight is that when you enter the building you see a reflection of the neon sign in the window of a bulletin-board display case on the opposite side of the hallway. People notice this right away. The light reflected off this window is polarized and we use this reflection as a polarization demo for several physics classes. Students view the reflected light through a piece of polarizing film.

And what does a crushed steel barrel have to do with a physics department's hallway display? And how did the barrel come to be crushed? Another sign directs the curious to the other end of the corridor for a descriptive answer — all the while walking past our display case and its neon "message."

Acknowledgment

The author wishes to thank Penny Davis for designing and maintaining the physics faculty display and the physics department machine shop staff for their excellent technical skills and support.

Canterbury's Physics Display Facility

John Campbell, Department of Physics, University of Canterbury,
Christchurch, New Zealand

Exhibitionism has its place. Take the fellow with bare legs protruding from a grubby gabardine overcoat. On the other hand, take physics; (or as we say, in these days of declining enrollments — take physics, *please*).

In first-year physics lectures we too often tend to bring to life the hoary definition of lecture notes, those that pass from the paper in front of the lecturer to the paper in front of the student without going through the brain of either. With an over-full syllabus to get through, we seldom digress to the lighthearted anecdotes that touch on the physics we are covering or pass on the excitement of research or the stimulation of physics today. The first-year student sees few glimpses of the future. At best we get to modern physics, which brings students up to about 1930. Often their only ray of sunshine is when the lecturer trots out a well-worn lecture demonstration. They perk up. Their interest is aroused. Particularly so if there is even the slimmest chance that right before their very eyes the demonstration will kill the lecturer.

In physics departments, lecture demonstrations are the norm for first-year classes. (We don't normally bother higher up, but that's another story.) The University of Canterbury has a long history in this field. Alexander Bickerton, the original professor of physical science, was a superb lecturer, showman, stimulator, communicator, and popularizer of science. He had learned by observing the great evangelists in full flight. Bicky owned more than 1000 lecture slides, invented display apparatus, and ran what would now be called a science centre. Little Bicky is the only academic in New Zealand to have inspired a future Nobel prize winner, Ernest Rutherford. (Not that it did Bicky much good — the university fired him a decade later.)

Lecture demonstrations have the drawback of not usually involving the student. They cover barely two-thirds of the unofficial motto of the hands-on science centres: *I read and I forget, I see and I remember, I do and I understand.* Besides, they are open to the charge that the shifty-eyed lecturer fiddled the outcome to get the result wanted. (During one public lecture on radioactivity, Ernest Rutherford was horrified to find that the radiation detectors and their crude electronic amplifiers did not respond when they should have. As an assistant moved across to check them Rutherford shouted "Leave them alone," whereupon the detectors registered a satisfactory count rate. The audience was impressed, not knowing that all they had witnessed was Rutherford's booming voice triggering the acoustically sensitive amplifier valves into producing noise.)

While not invading the corridors of power, physics demonstrations have seeped out to the corridors of schools and universities, as shown by *The Physics Teacher's* regular feature "Deck the Halls." Such corridor experiments spread, particularly in America, in the early 1960s. At Canterbury, the arrival of a new staff member (C.L. Miles), the shift of the science faculty to the new site at Ilam, and an enthusiastic lecture demonstrations technician (Anthony Lealand, who left in 1977 to become the Lucifer Fireworks and Searchlight Company) saw Canterbury's first corridor experiments in a large, glass-fronted cabinet outside our first-year lecture room. Control buttons, Variacs and Selsyn motors were mounted on a steel bracket protruding from each end at a height suitable to turn any passing male into a boy soprano.

These early interactive displays were true examples of the physicist's art: what it looks like doesn't matter; it's the experiment that counts. As a consequence, the equipment

Phys. Teach. 27, 526-529 (Oct. 1989)

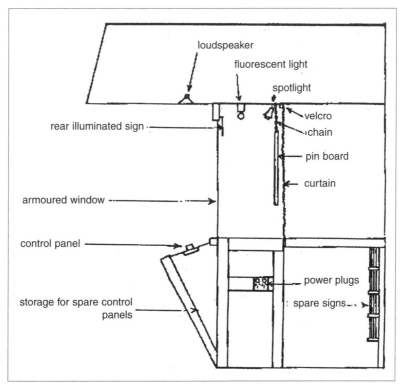

Fig. 1. A cross section through the display facility to show its layout.

looked as though made with chainsaw and sledgehammer. (An exaggeration, but they were often made from workshop scraps.) Explanatory notices were invariably handwritten with a felt pen. Homemade, lash-up, worn-out, make-do, rough, tatty: all were words display artists or exhibition designers would use if they lowered themselves to describe the presentation.

Consequently, by the early 1980s, when the case was also in decay with wood sagged, varnish bleached, and curtains faded, the whole effect gave the impression that no one cared. Unfortunately, at the time this was so.

All first-year physics students congregate outside the first-year lecture room at least three times a week, usually with a few spare minutes to fill in while waiting for the previous class to leave. Here is a captive audience waiting to be entertained and enlightened. In 1984, the arrival of a new demonstrations technician, Stephen Beuzenberg, and my burgeoning interest in museology and science centres, provided the impetus to upgrade the unit and its operation. We designed a new facility, which Stephen built during the summer vacation of 1984-85. He did a magnificent job.

Basic Philosophy

- The unit must be located in a place where first-year students congregate.

- Where at all possible, displays are to be interactive. The facility must be highly visible and advertise itself.

- Each display must be changed weekly so students see a dynamic facility.

- The unit should be designed to minimize the effort of changing displays.

- The highest standards of displays are to be used at all times.

- Each display should be eye-catching and interesting.

- Each display should attempt to get across just one physical point.

- A secure unit is needed for unattended operations involving valuable items.

Description of the New Display Facility

A cross section of the display facility (Fig. 1) shows the layout. The unit has four bays, each 1-m wide by 1-m high, which can be used singly or in multiples. All are loaded from the rear, with the aisle and access door allowing the passage of a standard trolley. Each bay has a bench depth of 50 cm except the one furthest from the access door, which runs the full depth of the unit. The bench nearest the door is of adjustable height and can be removed to be replaced by a trolley.

All viewing windows are of armored (luminated) glass to provide the high security needed for the unattended operation of valuable apparatus or objects. The end bays have side, as well as front, viewing.

The overhang helps reduce reflections from the windows. The ceiling space keeps the unit cool and houses two loudspeakers that can be used singly for any bay or in stereo for the central bays. Control panels at waist height are modular and easily changed. Made of aluminum plate, they are vinyl-covered for ease of cleaning. The inwards sloping timber under the panels prevents scuffmarks, thus keeping the front looking clean. Spare panels are stored behind the facing so they are readily accessible from the front.

Each bay has its own electrical system with a master time switch to turn the power off and on automatically on a weekly cycle. One unswitched socket is available for equipment that should not be turned off, for example, an aquarium pump. Power points and unsightly equipment are hidden under the benches. One fluorescent tube and two adjustable spotlights are mounted on the ceiling of each bay together with sundry hooks for hanging displays and panels.

Red velvet curtains worthy of the finest Parisian bordello form the backdrops and dividers of the bays. They attach to the ceiling by velcro. To shift one takes but a moment. If a bay is empty the curtain is shifted to the front behind a "Display under Preparation" sign. When setting up a display, the curtain hangs out of the way on the rear wall. Black velvet curtains are available for optics displays.

One of the firmest principles is that the display unit must at all times look well cared for. This policy has paid off since the unit is now in its fifth year of operation and has never been vandalized.

Labeling

Each bay is labeled by a rear-lit sign of large Letraset on translucent Perspex hanging from hooks. Twenty broad titles are available, covering the fairly specific "Holography" and "Magnetism" to the fairly general "physics" and, as a last resort, "miscellaneous." Those signs not in use are stored in easy-to-get-at racks under one bench.

Our display caters to a very select group who are all of the same educational standard. One advantage is that descriptions of displays are relatively easy to write. These are either typed with large letters and enlarged by photocopying or, increasingly, prepared on a word processor and laser printer, using paper that is often textured and sometimes colored. Wording is kept to a minimum. The descriptions are mounted in picture frames (gold frames to offset the plush red drapes). Two clips hold a backing plate in place, so changing an information sheet takes only seconds.

General Principles of the Displays

Each display is designed to be eye-catching, to make one point only, and to occupy a student for less than three minutes. If there is not a suitable display available, it is best to curtain off one bay with the excuse "Display under Preparation" than to leave an earlier one in. It is important that there be a change so that the students know it is worth looking at the unit at least once a week.

The size limit imposed on any object for display is 4-m long by 1-m high, which rules out electron-positron colliding rings but not much else.

Some displays reinforce classwork, thereby allowing students to repeat lecture demonstrations at their leisure, to give a closer view than is normally possible in large classes, to reinforce

Fig. 2. Students check out the physics displays at the University of Canterbury, New Zealand. The facility is situated in the foyer outside the lecture room used for first-year physics lectures. The displays in all four bays are changed weekly.

what should have been learned prior to coming to university, to show everyday examples of physics in action, or to point out applications in local industry.

Others show the way ahead: a slide/tape show of what jobs physicists do, the latest results of experiments that may be crucial to physics, eulogies of past graduates to get students thinking "Hmm...that could be me in a few years," undergraduate research projects, or the work of graduate students.

Some displays show the work at our field stations, one of which is in Antarctica. Others stimulate thought and discussion or are just for fun. April 1 should never pass by without being celebrated.

The field is wide. Anything that will help stimulate an interest in physics will be utilized. Some 200 displays are needed. With careful planning, very little preparation will be needed in the future for the bulk of the displays. These could be ordered by number, like meals in a Chinese restaurant, and trotted out by a junior technician. Such demonstrations are constructed especially for the display unit, each being stored self-contained in a labeled box. Only the control panels and power supplies are commu-

nal. A few displays dealing with current work have to be updated every year.

One aim is to have as many interactive displays as possible; three-quarters of them is the long-term goal, even if this means merely having a control button that turns on the display or turns on a spotlight to highlight the item of interest. For example, in a display of Rutherford artifacts a push button switched on an ornamental lamp whose lampshade had been made from Rutherford's earliest degree parchments.

Examples of Interactive Displays

Interactive displays include the operation of an aircraft air-speed indicator, optical spectra, the Curie point of a rare earth magnet, standing waves, Doppler radar door openers, the electron ferry, the speed of waves along a coaxial cable, simple heat engines, the flow of water through a constriction, background nuclear radiation, charging a capacitor, and the reflection of waves at boundaries.

Examples of Static Displays

One crowd-stopper is a two-bay display on electrical safety showing plugs and electrical appliances that have killed people. Others include using a bright-orange, egg-size disc to show students that they have a blind spot in each eye, a sample of the new high-temperature superconductors, ruby crystals grown by third-year students, library books of general physics interest, a He^3-cooled bolometer developed by a research student, smoke detectors that use α particles, the physics used in cartoons, a display of magnets (including magnetized uniform buttons from the Second World War together with accounts of escapes using these emergency compasses), a 10-week series updating weekly the latest news of the 1987 nova, sample responses to homework essays, a video segment on the physics of roller coasters and thrill machines, and a slide/tape presentation showing the activities of the third-year physics class.

Institute of Physics T-shirts have hung from a clothesline. A holographic kiss has been blown to passersby. Goldfish have refused to swim through a hoop. (This utilizes a simple principle of electromagnetic waves. It came from a book on window-stoppers loaned to me by the local magic shop so naturally I cannot divulge how it is done. The students are expected to try to work out why this illusion works.) One toy purchased from the magic shop appears at first sight to be a perpetual-motion machine. The students are asked to believe that or to figure out the basic principles of how it works.

Evaluation of Effectiveness

How effective is the display facility? My Mum thinks it is fantastic. Others think I am wasting my time and should get on with real physics (i.e., obscure research).

Evaluation of the worth of an activity is tricky to quantify. Eventually these questions have to be asked: Are we stimulating the students? Are they seeing into the future? Are they picking up more physics in their own time? I hope that this evaluation will be done sometime in the future by a professional evaluator of museum displays. At this stage all I can do is report my own biased views.

The facility is a success because the students use it (Fig. 2). Between lectures they crowd around the displays like academics at the staff club bar on half-price night. In between times, casual passersby such as cleaners and members of other departments stop off to see what's new.

A counter registers the number of times an interactive display is operated. For example, the electron ferry was operated 2200 times in a week, charging a capacitor 3311, impedance matching 3145, the operation of a watt-hour meter 3781, and determining the speed of a pulse down a coaxial cable 4500.

The facility is utilized by many nonstudents. During a vacation one optics display registered 307 operations on a day with no students in the area. A trade display surrounded the unit during the National Chemistry Conference, yet one of our electrical displays registered 1026 operations that week.

How accurate a record is the number of times a button is pushed? The counter makes no allowance for multiple pushes, students with a nervous twitch, or drunks. Only a cursory study was made. For some experiments one student would push the button more than once, but this was compensated for by the number of students watching at the time. Other displays seemed to encourage much multiple pushing. One day, when we can afford the luxury of continuous surveillance, the relevant correction factors possibly may be determined.

The interactive displays are only partially so. For security and safety, the student cannot handle the apparatus but can only operate remote controls. Hands-on equipment similar to that found in science centres is currently being built to supplement the display unit. These will be robust and accessible to the students by being mounted on the control panels.

Why should patrons of amusement parks have all the fun? Customers of physics need some too.

Acknowledgments

I wish to pay tribute to Stephen Beuzenberg for the major role he played in the design and establishment of the unit before moving on to an electronics position; to Bruce Bradshaw, the late Terry Rowe, and Wayne Smith for ideas used in the design; to the same four men for the construction of high-quality apparatus for displays; to Barbara Burst, the present lecture demonstration technician, and to Peter Cottrell and William Tobin for their astronomy displays.

The Physics Activities Center —
A Mini-Exploratorium

Dean Zollman, Department of Physics, Kansas State University,
Manhattan, KS 66506

At the introductory level, the Kansas State University Department of Physics offers five physics courses, one astronomy course, and one meteorology course to approximately 3900 students per year. These courses range from a nonmathematical physical science course to a calculus-based physics course. While every effort has been made to limit the size of individual sections, practical considerations require that individual lecture sections range in size from 100 to 150 students. To allow a more personal interaction with the students, the department offers laboratories and recitations of a maximum number of 30 students per section. While these 30-student sections provide greater opportunities for student-faculty interaction, the formalities of a classroom situation tend to restrict the oppor-

tunities for exploration into topics of interest to only a few students. Further, the geographical location of Kansas places the students far from any major science museum (such as The Museum of Science and Industry in Chicago or the Exploratorium[1] in San Francisco).

Recognition of this situation led the Department of Physics to establish the Physics Activities Center as a place to provide students the opportunity to "do their own thing" in physical science. The Center is a 30 by 18 ft room adjacent to the physics library and within a short distance of all the classrooms where physics courses are taught. With a donation of materials from local merchants and time from faculty and graduate students, the room (formerly a research laboratory) has been remodeled to provide a pleasant and comfortable atmosphere.

Fig. 1. The film loop carrells.

Phys. Teach. **12**, 213-216 (April 1974)

Fig. 2. The activities area in the center of the room.

Fig. 3. The activities area to the left of the entrance.

As a student enters the Physics Activities Center, he is standing beside the discussion area which contains a desk for an assistant (graduate or upper-level undergraduate student) who is available to help with questions about physics, an electronic calculator to aid the student with homework and laboratory calculations, and an end roll of newsprint for those discussions that involve a number of people. (By using newsprint, chalk dust has been eliminated in the room.)

Immediately in front of the student as he enters the room are five booths that contain either Super 8-mm film loop projectors or activities related to the study of light (Fig. 1). The department's library of film loops is shelved above these booths so that it is readily available to the student. Usually three or four carrells are devoted to film loop viewing while the others contain an optics-related experiment.

The remaining area in the room is set aside for the activities available to interested students (Figs. 2-3). With this room arrangement, the student who is performing an activity is not disturbed by the student who comes in for the specific purpose of asking a question, using the calculator, or viewing a film loop. On the other hand, the room is sufficiently open that most activities can be seen by the student as he enters the room. Frequently, a student who comes in just to ask a question notices something else

and gets "hooked."

Activities at the Center

Activities are designed to maximize involvement by students and minimize the "look-but-don't touch" neurosis. Students are encouraged to push, pull, and poke all equipment, to perform detailed measurements if they wish, and, when possible, to take the equipment home for further investigations of the physical world. To induce students to return several times during the semester, the available activities are changed on an irregular basis. No schedule is provided or announcements of changes made. Thus, students learn to wander in just to see if anything new has been placed in the center.

Materials used in the activities range from simple everyday items such as wine glasses and tape recordings to more sophisticated instructional apparatus such as the air table and the laser. Each piece of apparatus is accompanied by a short descriptive statement of the physical principles the activity demonstrates. The description usually contains comments that relate the activity to the physical world outside the classroom. (Equipment that can be misused, such as the laser, is marked with warnings about the dangers involved. The laser is located in a position that assures that the beam will not be directed into other areas of the room or into the eyes of students using it.)

Most apparatus used in the center is used also in the undergraduate laboratories or lecture demonstrations. After he performs a demonstration in his class, the lecturer is encouraged to place the apparatus in the Activities Center. Thus, no student needs to be satisfied to watch someone else try to rotate a spinning bicycle wheel; he can actually do it himself by walking a few steps to the Activities Center.

Other apparatus related to topics under discussion in the classroom and laboratory is available in the center. An interested student can take a topic just about as far as he wishes by using the apparatus in the center. He may study motion, collisions, and "kinetic theory" on an air table; optics with a He-Ne laser; wave motion with springs, strings and a ripple tank; and other topics with the appropriate equipment.

Just as a store offers "specials" to attract customers, activities that are designed to attract students are placed in the center. Materials related to light and sound are the most popular items of this nature. Students (and occasionally faculty) have been trapped by the oscilloscope trace which is "singing along" with Bob Dylan, George Harrison[2] or "Jesus Christ—Superstar."[3] Likewise, a rotating Polaroid disk[4] placed in front of a fixed polarizer and some crinkled cellophane has fascinated many people. While occasionally a student will merely view one of these activities and leave the center, more frequently he asks "How does this thing work?" When the explanation is followed by "Got anything else like that?" we believe we have helped rekindle the student's basic curiosity about the physical world.

An attractive item that brings students back several times is the "Crystal Garden." Since crystal growth is a rather slow process, students come in several times just to see how the crystals are doing. They can also perform experiments to watch crystals grow in a few minutes. (For example, silver and salol crystals can be grown in a few minutes.[5]) This particular activity has turned at least two freshmen from our physical science course into "crystal freaks." They have obtained books on crystals and are growing their own crystals in their dormitory rooms. This type of interest from even one student makes such an activity extremely valuable to those of us trying to make physics more enjoyable to the nonscience student.

Super-8 film loops are an integral part of the Activities Center. The student turned on by "The Tacoma Narrows Bridge Collapse"[6] or "Vibrating Soap Bubbles"[7] can investigate wave motion in other forms using materials in the center. In a less traditional format, film loops are part of activities demonstrating different frames of reference. A pendulum swinging over a turntable can be viewed by a student who, for practical purposes, is in the same frame as the pendulum. Because of limited space, we are not able to put the student in the rotating turntable frame. The next best thing to being there is viewing a film taken in the rotating system. A projector with this film is placed next to the turntable so that the student can compare the two frames of reference. A similar activity for linear frames of reference is being prepared.[8]

These activities and others seem to make physics more enjoyable for those students who visit the center. However, we wish to encourage students to observe physical phenomena outside the physics building as well as inside it. Thus, any piece of apparatus that can be moved can be checked out by students. These items can be used for whatever investigations of nature the student wishes to undertake. Table I indicates those items checked out during the first six months of operation. (Once again, the interest in sound and light is evident.) At present, no packaged experiments such as those developed by Brunschwig[9] are available for check-out. However, items for which some guidance has been provided (spectroscopes and telescopes) have proven most popular. Thus, check-out packages are being prepared.

Evaluation of the Center

During the first six months of the 1972-73 academic year 1773 students visited the Activities Center. The weekly attendance records (Fig. 4) indicate that the number of students visiting the Center has varied from a low of 48

Table I. Items check-out of Activities Center during first six months of 1972-73 academic year.

Item	Number of times checked out
Telescope	20
Spectroscope	17
Audio oscillator	6
Sound-level meter	3
Hologram	2
Gyroscope	1

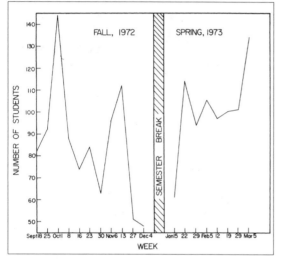

Fig. 4. The weekly attendance for the first six months of the 1972-73 academic year.

Table II. Results of survey of laboratory students.

Have you visited the Activities Center?

    Yes: 29.9%   *No: 70.1%*

$\left(\begin{array}{c} \text{following based on those who} \\ \text{answered yes to the above} \end{array} \right)$

How many times did you visit the Activities Center?

  Once: 36.9%   *Twice: 25.5%*   *Thrice: 14.7%*

Four or more: 22.8%

Do you recommend that your friends visit the Center?

    Yes: 79.2%   *No: 20.8%*

Will you visit the Center again if you take another physics course:

    Yes: 80.6%   *No: 19.4%*

Will you visit the Center again even if you do not take another physics course?

    Yes: 40.1%   *No: 59.9%*

Do you feel you learned physics in the Center that you did not learn elsewhere?

    Yes: 48.4%   *No: 51.6%*

Did your visits to the Center

  help raise your grade?   27.1%

  have no effect on your grade? 70.7%

  help lower your grade?   2.2%

to a high of 144 (during a week in which the Center received local publicity). During the fall semester, an average of about six students were in the Center every hour it was open. This number has increased slightly during the first half of the spring semester. This count of students is encouraging.

To obtain further information, all laboratory students were requested to complete a questionnaire at the end of the fall semester. (Since about 400 of our students do not enroll in laboratory, the sample is not quite complete.)

The striking features of the data (Table II) are these: A large number of students visited the Center at least once (more than 400 students); 63% of the visitors came back for another visit; a vast majority recommended that their friends visit the Center; and a rather large

minority (40.1%) say they will come back *even if they do not take another physics course.* Realistically, I do not expect 200 students not enrolled in any physics course to visit the Center. However, that many students were sufficiently turned on by the Center to state that they would return.

To attempt to determine what type of student was most likely to visit the Center, correlations were calculated between the questions in Table II and other questions such as "Did you work harder in this course than in others you are taking?" and "Is this course required for your curriculum?" The only strong correlation (coefficient = 0.51) is between the student's estimate of his grade and visiting the Center. Those students who believed they would receive a high laboratory grade were more likely to have visited the Center than those who expected low grades. However, essentially no correlation existed between number of visits and estimated grade. The lack of any other correlations indicates that the Center is attracting a wide variety of students. The Center seems to attract equally the students who take physics as a requirement and the students who choose it as an elective; the students who say they have a high level of interest in physics and the students who say they have little interest; the students who work hard in the physics course and the students who work not-so-hard. This attraction of students with such wide interests may be the Activities Center's biggest success. (In addition to the students surveyed, both students and faculty from the departments of Art, Biology, and Chemistry; the College of Education, and at least two local high schools have visited the Activities Center.)

Finally, of particular interest is the last question listed in Table II: "Did your visits to the Activities Center affect your grade?" While almost half of the visitors believed that they learned physics in the Center that they did not learn elsewhere, most of them did not attribute any change in their course grade to the visits. Since *no* assignments or credit are given for visits to the Center, one can conclude that the students came to the Activities Center simply because they enjoyed it.

Acknowledgments

An undertaking such as the Physics Activities Center requires the wholehearted support of all students, staff, and faculty involved in the introductory courses. Special acknowledgments are due C.E. Hathaway and J.D. Spears for their efforts in the beginning operation of the Center and George Athey for his efforts in designing and caring for the Crystal Garden.

I thank Cook Paint Company, The Gramaphone Works, JBL Inc., The Manhattan Mercury, Sears Roebuck and Company, Wal-Mart Discount Center, and Steven Zollman for contributions of items used in the Center.

References

1. Frank Oppenheimer, *Am. J. Phys.* **40**, 978 (1972).

2. George Harrison and His Friends, "Concert for Bangladesh" (Apple Records, Los Angeles, CA, 1972), STCX3385.

3. A.L. Weber and T. Rice, "Jesus Christ—Superstar" (Decca Records, New York, 1971), DXSA7206.

4. Available from Edmund Scientific Company, Barrington, NJ.

5. See PSNS Project Staff, *An Approach to Physical Science* (Wiley, New York, 1969), pp. 8-12.

6. F. Miller, Jr., "Tacoma Narrows Bridge Collapse" (Holt, Rinehart and Winston, New York, 1963).

7. Albert Baez, "Vibrating Soap Bubbles" (Encyclopedia Brittanica Educ. Corp., Chicago, IL, 1969).

8. Based on a design by W. Walton, private communication, and F. Wright and J. Rosenfeld, *A Demonstration Laboratory* (Education Research Center, M.l.T., Cambridge, MA, 1969), pp. 16-17.

9. F. Brunshwig, *AAPT Announcer* **2**, 25 (1972), and *AAPT Announcer* **1**, 26 (1971).

The Imagination Maze

Scott Welty and Jeff Rylander, Maine Township High School East,
2601 W. Dempster St., Park Ridge, IL 60068

It is one thing to learn the laws of physics; it is truly another to use the laws of physics in an effort to build a real-life machine! Last year our physics students welcomed the challenge of applying the physics that they would be learning throughout the school year in a huge "experiment," the building of a wall-sized vertical pinball machine that would illustrate laws of physics. This kinetic sculpture, known as the "Imagination Maze," was designed and constructed by about 80 physics students from Maine East High School (Fig. 1). Along with providing incredible hands-on experiences for our physics students, it was our hope that this project would also serve as a permanent, interactive display that demonstrates some laws of physics to our entire school body and the community.

Imagine a 3½-m vertical screw that students can turn in order to lift pool balls to the top of a display box built in a stairwell in the school's science wing. From there the balls descend through a labyrinth of ramps and loops, turning on lightbulbs, knocking over resetable dominos, activating an Atwood machine, playing musical instruments, incrementing a display counter to keep track of every ball that passes through this maze, and the list goes on. Though at its conception the goal of this project was quite clear in our minds, the final product was yet to be realized in the imaginations of our students. With the help of a Toyota TAPESTRY grant[1] and many generous donations by local industries, we were able to make our dream a reality. We found that raising the money to do this project was not nearly as hard as getting the machine to really work!

Beginning in September with blank pieces of paper, each of 10 student groups set out to dream what this machine could become. Each group, led by an AP Physics student, was made up of novice and experienced physics students alike. In late October, each student group presented their plans at a "Maze Planning Night." The students presented their plans to each other, to us, and to an advisory team of two mechanical engineers, an artist, and two metal workers. At the conclusion of the

Fig. 1. The "Imagination Maze."

Phys. Teach. **39,** 284-289 (May 2001)

Interactive Physics Demonstrations

AP Physics Maze Construction Team Leaders stand in front of the maze.

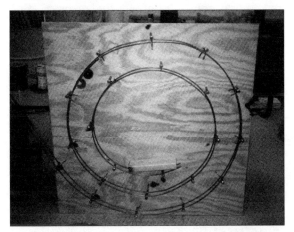

Fig. 2. Students began the construction process by creating prototypes of the various components of the Maze. Pictured here is the first version of the giant loop.

night, these professionals gave our students candid feedback. By November, the final plans had been mapped out on a life-size poster measuring 4 x 3 m. The student groups were now asked to prepare a budget within which they would work as they constructed the component that their team had "taken on." December and January were spent prototyping models of the various components (see Fig. 2). By February, students began constructing the final pieces to be installed and joined together as part of this interactive pinball machine. Each of the 10 student teams was given a rectangular piece of plywood onto which they were to fasten their components. These boards would eventually be pieced together to form the working machine itself. The project required

students from a variety of levels of physics to work with each other, to work with a group of professional engineers, and to make very real decisions regarding feasibility, cost, and aesthetics — along with considering the physics that each idea involved.

Though we recognize that you may not ever choose to tackle this exact project, we hope to give you a flavor of the truths of physics that came as a result of doing this project, truths from the minds of our students that we believe will never be forgotten.

Features of the Maze

The Screwlift

How do you actually raise a ball to the top of a 4-m high pinball machine? It was our intention from the beginning that if this display was to serve as a teaching tool for future physics classes as they investigate concepts such as the conservation of energy, each student who "operates" this maze should have to provide the energy required to lift each pool ball and thus the energy to run all components of the maze. With a handcrank mounted to a gearbox in our stairwell wall, students are able to turn a 3½-m vertical Archimedes' screw that lifts the pool balls. An "L-shaped" piece of Plexiglas protruding from the back provides the normal force required to rest each ball on the edge of the screw itself (see Figs. 3a and 3b). The screw was purchased from a Nebraska auger company[2] and is usually used for raising grain in silos.

The Plexiglas walls only extend as high as the ball is to be raised. At this point, since the walls no longer provide the normal force necessary to pin the ball against the screw, the ball simply falls away from the screw onto the first piece of track. Each pool ball is counted by a display counter before it enters a randomizer, four paths leading to many different tracks, making this a truly random pinball machine.

The Dominos

One of the most spectacular features of the maze is the resetable dominos (see Fig. 4). Despite much dissuading from us, our students believed that they could make this display work!

Fig. 3a. Balls feeding in at bottom of screwlift.

3a

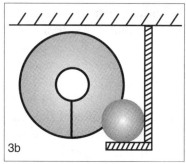

3b

Fig. 3b. Top view of screwlift and "L-shaped" Plexiglas wall illustrates how each pool ball is held in place while being lifted by the vertical screw.

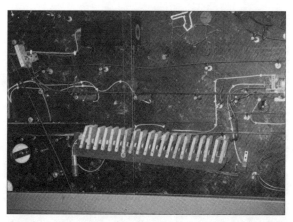

Fig. 4. Dominos tip when a kicker knocks over the domino on the right. After rotating through an angle necessary to reset all the dominos, the domino board returns to its original position and is ready for the next ball.

As a ball travels across an overhead track, it encounters a "kicker" that tips the domino on the right. Each domino tips the next until finally the left domino triggers a mechanical switch that is used to activate a motor that our students built out of a Lego Mindstorm kit.[3] With our homemade wooden dominos hinged on a board that pivots just to the left of the center of mass, the Lego motor allows the board and attached dominos to be rotated clockwise through an angle of about 70°. This angle is just over that required for the dominos to reset themselves to an upright position. With a set of gears and strings that our students added, the lowering process takes about one minute — an interesting contrast to the many fast-moving components of the maze. Once all the dominos have been reset, the motor reverses direction. One problem that concerned us early on was the fact that the string used to lower the domino board might slip or stretch over time and that the dominos would undershoot or over-

shoot the return position. This was solved by placing a second switch just above the right end of the pivoted domino board. The program code tells the motor to overshoot the reset position until it encounters this second switch. At that moment the motor reverses direction once again until it is off this switch and the dominos are ready for the next ball.

Electrical Circuits

A host of electrical circuits with lightbulbs, relays, timing chips, generators, and transformers fill the "empty" spaces of the Maze's back panel. With these circuits laid out in a schematic-like fashion, it is fairly easy to trace what each circuit is made to accomplish. One key feature is an overhead sign containing more than 100 7-W lightbulbs that spell out the words "MAINE EAST" whenever a ball triggers the "special switch." Not only was this a great exercise in wiring a combination circuit, we had an unexpected gem pop up in the process. Although a single switch is used to turn on all the letters at the same time, the length of time that each letter stays lit is determined by its own smaller timing circuit. (The diagram shown in Fig. 5 illustrates the timing circuit[4] that was constructed for each of the nine letters.) Despite the fact that identical resistor and capacitor values were used for each letter's circuit, yielding a time constant of $RC = 4.7$ seconds,

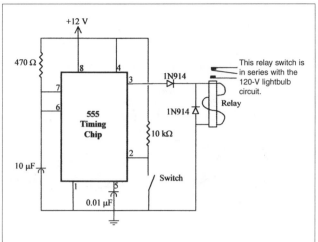

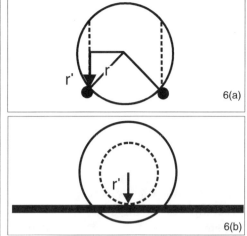

Fig. 5. Schematic of the timing circuit built by students to turn on various letters of the top sign when a pool ball passes across a switch.

Fig 6a. End view of ball on track. Notice that the distance from the center of the ball to its axis of rotation is less than the ball's radius.
Fig 6b. Side view of ball on track.

surprisingly, each letter went off at a different time. This became a wonderful lesson in propagation of error as the resistors and capacitors each present their own uncertainty to the circuit. What was meant to be a somewhat straightforward timing circuit became a whole lesson in uncertainties!

Real Life Loop-the-Loop

A major feature of the maze is a giant loop-the-loop. The students wanted a ball to begin near the upper left corner of the maze and travel to the lower right corner, performing three vertical loops in a spiral. Recall the basic physics for a sliding particle to complete a circular loop and not leave the track:

$$mgh = 1/2 \ mv^2 + mg(2R)$$

where h is the drop height and R is the radius of the outer loop. Add in the condition for staying on the track at the top where only gravity provides the centripetal acceleration:

$$g = v^2/R$$

and thus

$$h = 5/2 \ R.$$

If our available vertical space is about 3.5 m, how big a spiral can we hope to make? First of

all, if the ball makes the first loop it should have little problem making the second and third loops. If the outer loop has a radius of about 0.80 m, then h would have to be 2.0 m. Since we have 3.5 m to play with, we figured the "more than 2x factor" would allow us plenty of speed and extra energy for friction. This solution, however, is for a particle sliding down a ramp. We were going to have pool balls rolling down parallel rails. This brought up two questions: How much does the rolling energy add to our height requirements, and how does the fact that the ball is not rolling at its bottom change the fraction of the energy that goes into rolling energy?

As a starting point, we decided to calculate a new minimum height for rails that were placed as shown in Figs. 6a and 6b. The radii drawn to the two rails are perpendicular. The new energy equation, taking into account the moment of inertia of the ball as well as the condition for rolling without slipping, is

$$mgh = 1/2 \ mv^2 + mg(2R) + 1/2 \ I \ \omega^2$$

$$mgh = 1/2 \ mv^2 + mg(2R) + 1/2 \ (2/5 \ mr^2) \ v^2/r'^2,$$

where

$$r' = \frac{\sqrt{2}}{2}r$$

since the point of contact with the ramp is not at r but at r'. Finally, we discovered that for these conditions $h = 2.9\ R$. These parameters do not cause much of a required increase in the required height. Since we were well within actual dimensions of our display box, we proceeded with our idea and then designed track.

We needed a pretty simple design to support track from the back wall of the maze. This was true not only for the loop but for the maze in general. We decided to support all track with copper posts that were bolted to the plywood backing via T-nuts. Our supports allowed for both foreground and background tracks (see Fig. 7).

Atwood's Machine

At this point in their study of physics, our students were very familiar with the Atwood machine and felt like this would be a natural for the maze. They made no small plans, however, and desired their Atwood machine to use most of the vertical height of the maze. Of course, there has to be a way for the Atwood machine to reset itself so it could work again and again. The idea was for a ball to roll into a little carriage that would now weigh more than the counterweight and thus begin its downward trip. At the bottom, the ball would be ejected and the machine would begin its reverse trip. Seems simple enough....

It was easy to make a ball roll into our little carriage and then begin its downward trip in the Atwood machine. What if, however, a second ball approached the Atwood machine before the carriage returned? Our students built a teeter-totter arrangement whereby the Atwood carriage held up the left end of the teeter-totter. As the carriage begins to fall, the teeter-totter rotates counterclockwise, opening a passageway to another ramp that leads ultimately to the loop-the-loop. So, as long as the Atwood machine is in operation, balls that take this path from the randomizer are diverted. This makes the giant loop more of a treat as it takes two balls to go the same way in quick succes-

Fig. 7. Ball on track.

sion to get a ball to enter the loop-the-loop.

Now came the engineering. Three meters is a fair distance for an Atwood machine to accelerate. We began to worry about how large the final velocity might be. One way to control this is to have the two masses not too different. Although this seemed reasonable, the guy wires running vertically through the carriage to keep it aligned offered a significant amount of friction that had to be overcome. So how do you make the carriage side significantly heavier than the counterbalance side and yet not get excessive final velocities? With speed-dependent resistance, of course! We connected the Atwood pulley to a Genecon generator[5] shaft and then connected the generator's output to a lightbulb. With a small electrical resistance, we can control the terminal velocity of the machine and still have it significantly counterbalanced! Once a ball gets ejected from the carriage at the bottom, the Atwood returns to its position, lifting the teeter-totter bridge back into position, and is ready for the next ball.

Public Relations

A surprising bonus to this project was the wonderful recognition that it brought to our school. Countless local newspaper articles covered the student work in progress. We hosted a field trip for fourth graders of one of our feeder schools to whet their appetites for what high school science students can do. A group of senior citizens also came for a tour to see the project while it was being constructed, and then came again to see the finished product.

The Maze was unveiled at the conclusion of our science awards ceremony last spring. This proved to be a wonderfully exciting time as the first ball made its maiden voyage across the still shiny copper track. At the writing of this article, our counter reads just over 12,000 balls.

Student Cooperation

One of the most challenging things about this year-long construction project was finding ways to help the students use their time productively. We specifically refused to "build it for them." As the teachers, we prodded, suggested, gave instruction on technique and use of power tools, but did not do it for them. We were fortunate that there was an unused room right across the hall from the physics lab. We converted this room to our workshop and used some of our grant money for a table saw, drill press, band saw, and a variety of hand tools. This room became a beehive of activity after school, in the mornings, and even on Saturdays when the opening was getting close. Students liked learning how to use the tools and working with each other. As usual in big projects like this, a few students did a large percentage of the work. That's OK! You need them. As long as you are not robbing them from their other school responsibilities, take advantage of the extra-enthusiastic few who cannot be stopped.

The lessons learned in the building of this maze are wonderful life lessons. We re-learned (or learned for the first time) some basic physics. Even more, we learned how to use our time, how to work together, and how to overcome disappointment. We learned the real importance of accurate measuring … and, of course to measure twice and cut once! We learned that the textbooks only take you so far. After all, there is no set of directions for how to build a maze that is coming out of your collective imaginations. In the end, we had a wonderful machine that is a point of pride for the students who built it, an interesting conversation piece for those who pass by, and an inspiration for the physics students of the future.

References

1. The Toyota TAPESTRY program awards grant money to K-12 science teachers for innovative science projects that can be implemented over a one-year period.

2. The Nebraska augur company is called Egber's Farms, Inc., Hooper, NE.

3. We purchased the "Lego Mindstorms Robotics Invention System," a kit of programmable motors with mechanical switches and sensors that was incredibly useful. This can be purchased at toy stores for about $200.

4. This circuit diagram was adapted from one found in *Engineer's Mini-Notebook: 555 Timer IC Circuits*, p. 9, Radio Shack Catalog # 62-5010.

5. Genecon hand electric generator can be purchased from Sargent-Welch for about $52.

Resources

Teachers who wish to design and construct interactive physics exhibits for installation at their school have many resources available in addition to this book. One of the first places to look for more ideas should be local or regional science museums.

The exhibits in a science museum have much in common with a hallway exhibit. The main difference to keep in mind is that even though the traffic in a school hallway will be lighter than in a science museum, a science museum is usually well staffed while your school hallway will not be. This must be kept in mind when designing a "stand-alone" hallway exhibit. Many science museums publish books on their exhibits and some even have complete recipes for construction. The most comprehensive of these books are the cookbooks and snackbooks published by the Exploratorium in San Francisco.

Exploratorium Cookbook I by Raymond Bruman and the staff of the Exploratorium has "recipes" or specifications for building 82 exhibits related to light and images, vision, sound and hearing, electricity and magnetism, color, mechanics, and patterns. It also provides supplier and vendor lists.

Exploratorium Cookbook II by Ron Hipschman and the staff of the Exploratorium has specifications for building 52 exhibits on plant and animal behavior, exponentials and additional ones on topics covered in *Cookbook I*.

Exploratorium Cookbook III by Ron Hipschman and the staff of the Exploratorium rounds out the series with 67 exhibits. Topics covered include mathematics and neurophysiology in addition to the traditional fields of physics.

In addition to these large cookbooks, the Explorarorium sells "snackbooks" developed by Paul Doherty, Don Rathjen, and the Exploratorium teacher institute. The snacks in the snackbooks are classroom-sized versions of the same science exhibits at the Exploratorium. Many of these could be ideal for a small-scale hallway exhibit.

A companion to the snackbooks is offered called *Hands on Science,* a teacher's guide to student-built experiments and the Exploratorium science snackbook.

All of these books are available from:

The Exploratorium
3601 Lyon St.
San Francisco, CA 94123
(415)-EXP-LORE

or go to their website, www.exploratorium.edu for prices and ordering instructions, as well as more details.

Another great resource on building and maintaining physics hallway exhibits is a set of two books by Dick Crane. The first is *Explore and Discover: The Ann Arbor Hands-On Museum Exhibits Guide*. This book has descriptions, photographs, and drawings of 67 exhibits at the museum. Details of the actual construction are not included in this book.

However, there is a companion book, *How to Build It and Keep It Working*. Full construction and maintenance information for 32 of the exhibits is included in this volume. In addition to detailed blueprints and instructions, the author also includes graphic information on "What to do?" And "What is happening?" There are also sections on each exhibit that address maintenance problems. The titles of these sections include:

"What problems can there be?"
"What happens if the controls don't work?"
"What happens if the exhibit stops working?"

In other words, everything you need to know about building exhibits!

Information on ordering both books can be obtained from:

The Ann Arbor Hands-On Museum
219 East Huron St.
Ann Arbor, MI 48104